Directory of Doctors

Practicing

Advanced

Natural Medicine

By

The Staff of

University Medical Research Company

University Medical Research Publishers
Tempe, Arizona

Library of Congress Cataloging-in-Publication Data

Main entry under title:

Directory of doctors practicing advanced natural medicine.

1. Directory—Doctors—Addresses
2. Directory—Doctors—Addresses. I. University
   Medical Research

ISBN 0-9638714-2-0

Printed and bound in the United States of America.

10 9 8 7 6 5 4 3

Directory of Doctors

Practicing

Advanced

Natural Medicine

FOREWORD

What's the difference between conventional medicine and natural medicine?

Probably the simplest explanation is conventional medicine tries to alleviate the symptoms while natural medicine treats the cause of disease. If you have gall-bladder problems, the conventional doctor cuts out the gall-bladder and says, *"Now you won't have gall-bladder problems any more!"*

Of course, he didn't tell you that you'll suffer with digestive problems for the rest of your life because the gall-bladder is very important to a properly functioning digestive system.

The natural medicine doctor knows that most gall-bladder problems are caused by the accumulation of gallstones. The stones are usually oxalate compounds which are formed as a result of eating certain foods. Therefore, he will examine your diet, probably recommend that you avoid certain foods, eat others that you may need, give you nutritional supplements and natural remedies that will help the stones dissolve and your gall-bladder function better.

Which doctor would you choose: the one who treats the symptom, or the one who tries to alleviate the cause?

There are very few prescription drugs that correct the cause of diseases. The major exception is antibiotics which kill bacteria-caused disease. Unfortunately, they kill most of the bacteria in our bodies, of which many are friendly and have important functions. For example, a certain bacteria prevents yeast infections, and for that reason, yeast infections are a common side effect of taking antibiotics.

Also, often conventional doctors prescribe antibiotics for viral infections, but antibiotics don't have any effect on viruses. Putting it more simply, most prescription drugs don't cure anything. All they do is make you more comfortable while your body cures itself! Ask any doctor. He or she will have to admit that it is true.

The public can be fooled for a while but not forever. In the last 10 years, we've seen a growing rebellion against the "cut and drug" medical establishment. This has been brought about by the frustration of patients being treated for chronic diseases. Most patients don't get any better and usually get worse while suffering the side effects of prescription drugs.

Since the body cures itself of the majority of ailments if it is allowed to function properly, the focus of the doctor should be on keeping his patients' bodies in optimal health— especially the immune system. A strong immune system will fight off most diseases.

That is how doctors who practice natural medicine approach an ailment. They look at the whole person. Just because you have a headache doesn't necessarily mean the cause originates in your head. It may mean that you have a food allergy, stress, a nutritional imbalance or deficiency, an adverse reaction to prescription or over-the-counter drugs or many other reasons.

In conventional medical schools, students are not taught about food allergies, stress-caused illnesses or nutrition. In fact, they are told that no one needs vitamin or mineral supplements if they eat a balanced diet. Yet literally dozens of controlled clinical studies show that the majority of patients suffering from the most common chronic diseases (such as arthritis, heart disease, circulatory problems, high cholesterol, cataracts, poor memory, Alzheimer's and many more) have deficiencies of common vitamins and minerals.

Even if you eat a balanced diet, there are two reasons why you can have deficiencies. First, studies by the National Food Review Board showed that up to 93% of the nutrients in food are destroyed by cooking, canning, freezing and processing food.

Second, even fresh foods have very low levels of vital minerals even when eaten raw. The reason has to do with commercial fertilizers. Prior to 1945, most farmers used manure to fertilize crop land. The manure put back most of the minerals extracted from the soil by plants and vegetables. Commercial fertilizers contain nitrogen, potassium and phosphate. Minerals important to humans such as calcium, magnesium, zinc, selenium, copper, chromium, etc., are missing. You can see why a few years of farming with commercial fertilizers has left no nutrients in the soil, and none in the fruits and vegetables we eat.

Beware of The Big Business of Medicine

Prescription drugs and surgeries are huge businesses that bring in billions of dollars a year. Obviously, this big money crowd doesn't want to cut off its profit with inexpensive and effective corrections of the causes of diseases. A Harvard Medical School study and one conducted by the government's Office of Technological Assessment found that up to 85% of surgeries were unnecessary or ineffective.

For example, the popular heart bypass surgery costs an average of $50,000, yet conventional doctors will admit that it only postpones the problem for a few years. On the other hand, natural medicines' chelation therapy costs only $3,000 to $5,000 and corrects the cause in most cases, if done in conjunction with lifestyle modification.

If you are unfamiliar with natural medicine techniques, and therefore, uneasy; explain this to the natural medicine doctor. He or she will understand because many of them began their careers in conventional medicine. In many cases, they will allow you to continue your prescription drugs until you are comfortable with the natural remedies.

If you are currently being treated by a conventional doctor, you should get an opinion from a doctor specializing in natural medicine. It could make you a lot healthier and might save your life—even if you have cancer.

Although natural medicine is a whole body medicine, many specialists from conventional medicine have converted to natural medicine. Often, their specialty is not listed in Yellow Page directories because of the nature of this medical field. However, the number of doctors in natural medicine is small, and they usually know each other and their specialties. Therefore, if you have special needs, they will know who to send you to.

We created this directory because it is difficult to determine in most Yellow Pages just which doctors are in natural medicine. Chiropractors and acupuncturists are considered in the natural health field, but because they are so numerous in most cities and have special headings in Yellow Page directories, we have not listed them in this directory.

Contents

ALABAMA

DR. MARGUERITE CLEVELAND
1337A HIGHWAY 119, ALABASTER, AL

DR. DON BRYAN
P.O .BOX 1857, ALABASTER, AL

DR. SAMUEL FISCHER III
1016 18TH ST. S., BIRMINGHAM, AL

DR. SHASHIDHAR SHETTAR
619 19TH ST. S., RM. N477, BIRMINGHAM, AL

DR. JOHN FARMER
2156 GREEN SPRINGS HWY. S., BIRMINGHAM, AL

DR. JOAN SCOTT LOWE
2038 22ND CT. S., BIRMINGHAM, AL

DR. ROBERT C. DOEKEL
P.O. BOX 130902, BIRMINGHAM, AL

GLENWOOD HEALTH SERVICES
150 GLENWOOD LN., BIRMINGHAM, AL

DR. C. O. TRUSS
2614 HIGHLAND AVE. S., BIRMINGHAM, AL

DR. GUS J. PROSCH
759 VALLEY ST., BIRMINGHAM, AL

DR. ANDREW M. BROWN
411 YORKSHIRE DR., BIRMINGHAM, AL

DR. DAVID G. DAVILA
619 19TH ST. S., RM. N477, BIRMINGHAM, AL

DR. ANN B. McDOWELL
P.O. BOX 6907, DOTHAN, AL

DR. ALAN D. PRINCE
P.O. BOX 6987, DOTHAN, AL

DR. ANDREW M. BROWN
515 S. 3RD ST., GADSDEN, AL

DR. PAUL LEGRAND
101 SIVLEY RD. S.W., HUNTSVILLE, AL

DR. ALAN H. ARRINGTON
250 CHATEAU DR. S.W., STE. 225, HUNTSVILLE, AL

DR. ROBERT E. MCALISTER
P.O. BOX 769, MILLBROOK, AL

DR. ROBERT DAWKINS
P.O. BOX 2144, MOBILE, AL

DR. JOSEPH B. MILLER
5901 AIRPORT BLVD., MOBILE, AL

DR. LAWRENCE S. SCHOEN
3719 DAUPHIN ST., MOBILE, AL

DR. DAVID P. FRANCO
2105 E. SOUTH BLVD., MONTGOMERY, AL

DR. RICHARD M. SNOW
701 UNIVERSITY BLVD. E., TUSCALOOSA, AL

DR. HUMPHRY OSMOND
200 UNIVERSITY BLVD., TUSCALOOSA, AL

ALASKA

DR. WILLIAM F. RISCH
520 W 41ST AVE., STE. 101, ANCHORAGE, AK

DR. TORREY SMITH
2216 CULVER PL, ANCHORAGE, AK

DR. F. R. MANUEL
4141 B ST., STE. 209, ANCHORAGE, AK

DR. HOPE WING
520 E. 34TH AVE., STE. 305, ANCHORAGE, AK

DR. CARY JASPER
1407 W. 31ST AVE., ANCHORAGE, AK

DR. MARY A. MINOR
4050 LAKE OTIS PKY., STE. 205, ANCHORAGE, AK

DR. SANDRA DENTON
4115 LAKE OTIS PKY., #200, ANCHORAGE, AK

DR. ROBERT ROWEN
615 E. 82ND AVE., STE. 300, ANCHORAGE, AK

DR. SANDRA VAISVIL
P.O. BOX 407, DILLINGHAM, AK

DR. RUTH BAR-SHALOM
222 FRONT ST., FAIRBANKS, AK

DR. SCOTT L. JAMISON
369 S. FRANKLIN ST., STE. 300, JUNEAU, AK

DR. GLENNA WILDE
P.O. BOX 22857, JUNEAU, AK

DR. TOBY WHEELER
P.O. BOX 20063, JUNEAU, AK

DR. PATTON D. PETTIJOHN
P.O. BOX 878894, WASILLA, AK

DR. ROBERT MARTIN
P.O. BOX 870710, WASILLA, AK

ARIZONA

DR. FORREST WELLINGTON
27407 N. 46TH ST., CAVE CREEK, AZ

DR. PATRICK SARTZ
3120 N. ARIZONA AVE., #1201, CHANDLER, AZ

DR. DENNIS CRENSHAW
P.O. BOX 1681, COTTONWOOD, AZ

DR. MARK JAMES
809 N. HUMPHREYS ST., FLAGSTAFF, AZ

DR. MARY C. POORE
809 N. HUMPHREYS ST., FLAGSTAFF, AZ

DR. ROBERT MORRISSEY
516 N. HUMPHREYS ST., FLAGSTAFF, AZ

DR. LLOYD D. ARNOLD
4901 W. BELL RD., STE. 2, GLENDALE, AZ

DR. JOHN L. BREWER
5002 W. GLENDALE AVE., STE. 101, GLENDALE, AZ

DR. FRANCIS J. WOO, JR.
60 RIVIERA DR., LAKE HAVASU CITY, AZ

DR. PAUL BARNARD
1400 S. DOBSON RD., MESA, AZ

DR. THOMAS BRADBURY
2051 S. DOBSON RD., #17-183, MESA, AZ

DR. KENNETH HATFIELD
220 N. STAPLEY DR., MESA, AZ

DR. WILLIAM W. HALCOMB
4323 E. BROADWAY, STE. 109, MESA, AZ

DR. S. W. MEYER
P.O. BOX 1870, PARKER, AZ

DR. MIRIAM GILBERT
P.O. BOX 882, PATAGONIA, AZ

DR. STEPHEN M. DAVIDSON
1303 W. BETHANY HOME RD., PHOENIX, AZ

DR. DONALD R. BETTNER
1137 W. MCDOWELL RD., PHOENIX, AZ

DR. MICHAEL J. CRONIN
2530 E. INDIAN SCHOOL RD., PHOENIX, AZ

DR. EVA URBANIAK
1901 E. OSBORN RD., APT. 102, PHOENIX, AZ

DR. JEFFREY S. GITT
3929 E. BELL RD, PHOENIX, AZ

DR. RICK CHESTER
825 E. ORANGE DR., PHOENIX, AZ

DR. ABRAM BER
20635 N. CAVE CREEK RD., PHOENIX, AZ

DR. ROBERT L. GEAR, JR.
3543 N. 7TH ST., PHOENIX, AZ

DR. H. C. PURTZER
13825 N. 7TH ST., STE. H, PHOENIX, AZ

DR. JOHN C. REED
4538 N. 40TH ST., PHOENIX, AZ

DR. BERNARD LEVINE
1111 E. MCDOWELL RD., PHOENIX, AZ

DR. STANLEY R. OLSTZYN
3610 N. 44TH ST., STE. 210, PHOENIX, AZ

DR. KYLE H. CRONIN
2530 E. INDIAN SCHOOL RD., PHOENIX, AZ

DR. KONRAD KAIL
13832 N. 32ND ST., STE. C, PHOENIX, AZ

DR. BRUCE SHELTON
2525 W. GREENWAY RD., Fl 3RD, PHOENIX, AZ

DR. TERRY S. FRIEDMANN
2701 E. CAMELBACK RD., STE. 381, PHOENIX, AZ

DR. DANA KEATON
5702 N. 4TH PL., PHOENIX, AZ

DR. RALPH F. HERRO
5115 N. CENTRAL AVE., PHOENIX, AZ

DR. DANA MYATT
815 N. 52ND ST., APT. 2153, PHOENIX, AZ

DR. ARTHUR SCHIMELFENIG
926 E. MCDOWELL RD., STE. 21, PHOENIX, AZ

DR. GENE SCHROEDER
2063 THUMB BUTTE RD., PRESCOTT, AZ

DR. ROBERT M. MYERS
805 MILLER VALLEY RD., PRESCOTT, AZ

DR. ROBERT C. UPCHURCH
1055 RUTH ST., STE. 6, PRESCOTT, AZ

DR. MARLEY ROBERTSON
315 W. GOODWIN ST., PRESCOTT, AZ

DR. DREW COLLINS
8030 E. YAVAPAI RD., PRESCOTT VALLEY, AZ

DR. LESLIE AXELROD
8030 E. YAVAPAI RD., PRESCOTT VALLEY, AZ

DR. GORDON JOSEPHS
7315 E. EVANS RD., SCOTTSDALE, AZ

DR. CLARK H. HANSEN
10615 N. HAYDEN RD., STE. 100, SCOTTSDALE, AZ

DR. H. F. FELLOWS
3604 N. WELLS FARGO AVE., #M, SCOTTSDALE, AZ

DR. STANLEY OLSZTYN
3200 N. HAYDEN RD., SCOTTSDALE, AZ

DR. LOUISE D. GUTOWSKI
8300 N. HAYDEN RD., STE. 112, SCOTTSDALE, AZ

DR. KENT L. POMERORY
9755 N. 90TH ST., #A205, SCOTTSDALE, AZ

DR. HARVEY BIGELSON
9755 N. 90TH ST., #A-200, SCOTTSDALE, AZ

DR. CHERYL A. HARTER
49 BELL ROCK PLZ., STE. E, SEDONA, AZ

DR. LESTER ADLER
P.O. BOX 1565, SEDONA, AZ

DR. SILENA HERON
2081 W. U.S. HIGHWAY 89A, #1-C, SEDONA, AZ

DR. GLORIA THORESON
P.O. BOX 1544, SUN CITY, AZ

DR. GARRY GORDON
5535 S. COMPASS RD., TEMPE, AZ

DR. LOUISE D. BURATOVICH
2435 E. SOUTHERN AVE., STE. 9, TEMPE, AZ

DR. FARRA SWAN
2435 E. SOUTHERN AVE., STE. B, TEMPE, AZ

DR. MICHAEL R. ANCHARSKI
10950 E. CALLE VAQUEROS, TUCSON, AZ

DR. STUART F. QUAN
1501 N. CAMPBELL AVE., TUCSON, AZ

DR. KENNETH S. BLACKMAN
3002 E. FLORENCE DR., TUCSON, AZ

DR. TERI L. DAVIS
6342 E. CALLE LUNA, TUCSON, AZ

DR. FRANCIS J. BRINKER
6417 E. HAYNE ST., TUCSON, AZ

DR. AUTUMN HOLDER
1001 N. SWAN RD., TUCSON, AZ

DR. ILENE M. SPECTOR
540 W. PRINCE RD., STE. F, TUCSON, AZ

DR. GENE SCHUMUTZER
2425 N. ALVERNON WAY, TUCSON, AZ

DR. ELLIS V. BROWNING
1150 W. 24TH ST., STE. F, YUMA, AZ

ARKANSAS

DR. EDWARD C. HILL JR
HC 72 BOX 60, CLINTON, AR

DR. LAURA KOEHN
2100 GREEN ACRES RD., FAYETTEVILLE, AR

DR. SUZANNE FROMHERZ
327 W. MEADOW ST., FAYETTEVILLE, AR

DR. WILLIAM WRIGHT
1 MERCY LN., STE. 211, HOT SPRINGS, AR

ST VINCENT'S MEDICAL CENTER
2 SAINT VINCENT CIR., LITTLE ROCK, AR

DR. NORBERT J. BECQUET
115 W. 6TH ST., LITTLE ROCK, AR

DR. KARL H. KARLSON
800 MARSHALL ST., LITTLE ROCK, AR

DR. ROBYNN ZINSER
5305 KAVANAUGH BLVD., LITTLE ROCK, AR

DR. CHARLES SWINGLE
103 NATHAN ST., MARKED TREE, AR

DR. JOHN L. GUSTAVUS
4721 E. BROADWAY ST., NORTH LITTLE ROCK, AR

DR. AUBREY M. WORRELL JR
3900 S. HICKORY ST., PINE BLUFF, AR

DR. DOTY MURPHY
812 DORMAN ST., SPRINGDALE, AR

CALIFORNIA

DR. GEORGIE PRYAL
1414 EVERETT ST., ALAMEDA, CA

DR. ROGER N. MORRISON
828 SAN PABLO AVE., ALBANY, CA

DR. MATTHEW J. VUKSINICH
828 SAN PABLO AVE., ALBANY, CA

DR. DON CANAVAN
555 PIERCE ST., APT. 724, ALBANY, CA

DR. ROSS B. GORDON
405 KAINS AVE., ALBANY, CA

DR. SANDRA MAGIN
1172 SAN PABLO AVE., #201, ALBANY, CA

DR. ALLEN C. NEISWANDER
1508 S. GARFIELD AVE., ALHAMBRA, CA

DR. STUART MENN
1101 S. ANAHEIM BLVD., ANAHEIM, CA

DR. DAVID L. STEPHENSON
216 W. CYPRESS ST., ANAHEIM, CA

DR. VALERIE LONG
P.O. BOX 17101, ANAHEIM, CA

DR. DANIEL BEILIN
9057 SOQUEL DR., #3, APTOS, CA

DR. EVONNE BARRETT-PHILLIP
34 SUNNYBRAE CTR, ARCATA, CA

DR. ZANE KIME
1212 HIGH ST., STE. 204, AUBURN, CA

DR. DALE H. POWERS
3728 GRASS VALLEY HWY., AUBURN, CA

DR. RALPH G. SEIBLY
1311 COLUMBUS ST., BAKERSFIELD, CA

DR. JOHN CLAYPOOL
400 CHESTER AVE., BAKERSFIELD, CA

DR. ANA C. VERTEL
1176 SPRUCE ST., BERKELEY, CA

DR. STEPHEN SPORN
P.O. BOX 9946, BERKELEY, CA

DR. LISA FREDRIKSEN
1717 ALCATRAZ AVE., BERKELEY, CA

DR. MICHAEL LESSER
2340 PARKER ST., BERKELEY, CA

DR. STEVEN LANGER
3031 TELEGRAPH AVE., BERKELEY, CA

DR. ELLEN GUNTHER
2615 ASHBY AVE., BERKELEY, CA

DR. FRANCES KALFUS
2615 ASHBY AVE., BERKELEY, CA

aDR. JEFFREY GRAPPO
1534 SOLANO AVE., BERKELEY, CA

DR. JOAN POWELSON
570 THE ALAMEDA, BERKELEY, CA

DR. BONNIE BRIGID
941 HILLDALE AVE., BERKELEY, CA

DR. SUSAN ISAACSON
1508 BONITA AVE., BERKELEY, CA

DR. BRENDA J. BEELEY
724 GILMAN ST., BERKELEY, CA

DR. MARK HOLMES
301 N. CANON DR., STE. 215, BEVERLY HILLS, CA

DR. EVE CAMPANELLI
8530 WILSHIRE BLVD., STE. 209, BEVERLY HILLS, CA

DR. REX WILSON
8383 WILSHIRE BLVD., STE. 360, BEVERLY HILLS, CA

DR. INSTITUTE GERSON
P.O. BOX 430, BONITA, CA

DR. RUDOLPH ALSLEBEN
4364 BONITA RD., #200, BONITA, CA

DR. TIMOTHY A. KERSTEN
P.O. BOX 1460, BURNEY, CA

DR. AURA MANN
24009 VENTURA BLVD., STE. 250, CALABASAS, CA

DR. LORIE PHILLIPS
3801 LAS POSAS RD., STE. 211, CAMARILLO, CA

DR. CAROL A. SHAMLIN
621 E. CAMPBELL AVE., STE. 11A, CAMPBELL, CA

DR. VINCENT MARK
4145 CLARES ST., CAPITOLA, CA

DR. SHARON HECKERT
716 CAPITOLA AVE., STE. A, CAPITOLA, CA

DR. CARL M. BENGS
2910 JEFFERSON ST., STE. 100, CARLSBAD, CA

DR. BERNARD MCGINITY
6945 FAIR OAKS BLVD., CARMICHAEL, CA

DR. RICHARD STACK
6501 COYLE AVE., CARMICHAEL, CA

DR. RICHARD TURNER
1324 MANGROVE AVE., STE. 110, CHICO, CA

DR. KURT DONSBACH
738 DESIGN CT., STE. 301, CHULA VISTA, CA

DR. RODRIGO RODRIGUEZ
1180 WALNUT AVE., CHULA VISTA, CA

DR. MARGUERITE M. HUNG
353 H ST., STE. E, CHULA VISTA, CA

GENESIS WEST CLINIC
P.O. BOX 3460, CHULA VISTA, CA

DR. MITCH CHAVEZ
1220 E. WASHINGTON ST., STE. 24, COLTON, CA

DR. TIMOTHY GROTHMAN
2975 TREAT BLVD., STE. B1, CONCORD, CA

DR. BILL GRAY
2108 GRANT ST., STE. 2, CONCORD, CA

DR. KEELING-FRIEDMA
2919 RICHARD AVE., CONCORD, CA

DR. ELIZA LADYZHENSKY
760 WASHBURN AVE., STE. 11, CORONA, CA

DR. REED D. CHRISTOPHERSON
2711 E. COAST HWY., STE. 206, CORONA DEL MAR, CA

DR. MICHAEL ROSENBAUM
45 SAN CLEMENTE DR., CORTE MADERA, CA

DR. CHUCK RUDY
645 TAMALPAIS DR., CORTE MADERA, CA

DR. JEFF ANDERSON
45 SAN CLEMENTE DR., CORTE MADERA, CA

DR. STANLEY HANSEN
440 FAIR DR., STE. J, COSTA MESA, CA

DR. KATHERINE AMBER
8879 OLD REDWOOD HWY., COTATI, CA

DR. JAMES PRIVITERA
105 N. GRANDVIEW AVE., COVINA, CA

DR. CECILE LEVIN
11215 HANNUM AVE., CULVER CITY, CA

DR. FAWN CHRISTIANSON
21721 GRANADA AVE., CUPERTINO, CA

DR. CHARLES K. DAHLGREN
1800 SULLIVAN AVE., RM. 604, DALY CITY, CA

DR. HITEN H. SHAH
21343 COLD SPRING LN., #421, DIAMOND BAR, CA

DR. MARK J. BUCHFUHRER
8300 TELEGRAPH RD., DOWNEY, CA

DR. WILLIAM J. SACCOMAN
505 N. MOLLISON AVE., STE. 103, EL CAJON, CA

DR. CAROL JESSUP
6500 FAIRMOUNT AVE., EL CERRITO, CA

DR. MERLIN LEACH
500 MAIN ST., EL SEGUNDO, CA

DR. ELIZABETH REES
9140 BRUCEVILLE RD., ELK GROVE, CA

DR. JACQUES DEZAVELLE
1118 2ND ST., ENCINITAS, CA

DR. BONNIE MARSH
511 1ST ST., STE. 217, ENCINITAS, CA

DR. PRISCILLA SLAGLE
16542 VENTURA BLVD., STE. 306, ENCINO, CA

DR. LEONARD A. KLEPP
16311 VENTURA BLVD., STE. 725, ENCINO, CA

DR. GARY M. VERIGIN
1415 OKLAHOMA AVE., ESCALON, CA

DR. LAWRENCE F. SCHNELL
1261 MOUNTAIN PARK PL., ESCONDIDO, CA

DR. BENJAMIN KANTER
555 E. VALLEY PKY., ESCONDIDO, CA

DR. JACQUELYN J. WILSON
536 BROTHERTON RD., ESCONDIDO, CA

DR. PATRICK MCCARTY
1122 M ST., EUREKA, CA

DR. MURIEL R. BRAMWELL
2435 CHESTER ST., EUREKA, CA

DR. DAVID K. WARKENTIN
P.O. BOX 39, FAIRFAX, CA

DR. ERHARDT ZINKE
2131 WINTERWARM DR., FALLBROOK, CA

DR. LAWRENCE BADGLEY
1020 FOSTER CITY BLVD., FOSTER CITY, CA

DR. ROBERT J. BROADWELL
18837 BROOKHURST ST., STE. 205, FOUNTAIN VALLEY, CA

DR. JORDAN WEISS
11770 WARNER AVE., STE. 110, FOUNTAIN VALLEY, CA

DR. ROBERT L. GARABEDIAN
1616 W. SHAW AVE., STE. C2, FRESNO, CA

DR. DAVID J. EDWARDS
360 S. CLOVIS AVE., FRESNO, CA

DR. JUSTINE A. PETRIE
101 E. VALENCIA MESA DR., FULLERTON, CA

DR. LUIS MCNABB
101 E. VALENCIA MESA DR., FULLERTON, CA

DR. ROBERT ROETHE
101 E. VALENCIA MESA DR., FULLERTON, CA

DR. ELMER THOMASSEN
22807 BARTON RD., GRAND TERRACE, CA

DR. BARBARA DAKIN
14645 MEADOW DR., GRASS VALLEY, CA

DR. ALAN G. BROWN
673 S. AUBURN ST., GRASS VALLEY, CA

DR. JUDITH FENLEY
P.O. BOX 588, GRATON, CA

DR. FLOYD H. BRIGHAM
P.O. BOX 1228, GROVELAND, CA

DR. ELIZABETH GILIGA
788 MARIN AVE., HAYWARD, CA

DR. STEVEN I. SUBOTNICK
19682 HESPERIAN BLVD., HAYWARD, CA

DR. CECIL A. BRADLEY
27206 CALAROGA AVE., STE. 205, HAYWARD, CA

DR. ROBERT BUCKLEY
1320 APPLE AVE., #203, HAYWARD, CA

DR. MICHAEL J. LIPELT
8201 W. DRY CREEK RD., HEALDSBURG, CA

DR. DAVID B. JONES
835 HEALDSBURG AVE., HEALDSBURG, CA

MEADOWLARK HEALTH CENTER
26126 FAIRVIEW AVE., HEMET, CA

DR. LOREE BABICH
611 SAN BENITO ST., HOLLISTER, CA

DR. JEANETTE SHRANK
1430 DIABLO DR., APT. 3, HOLLISTER, CA

DR. JOAN M. RESK
18821 DELAWARE ST., STE. 203, HUNTINGTON BEACH, CA

DR. GARY ARCHER
2670 E. GAGE AVE., STE. 1, HUNTINGTON PARK, CA

DR. ROBERT L. HARMON
43576 WASHINGTON ST., INDIO, CA

DR. BRUCE K. BATTLESON
18124 CULVER DR., STE. H, IRVINE, CA

DR. HOLLIS H. KING
4150 REGENTS PARK ROW, LA JOLLA, CA

DR. MILTON ERMAN
10666 N. TORREY PINES RD., LA JOLLA, CA

DR. LARRY AYERS
P.O. BOX 158, LA MESA, CA

DR. ALEX Y. CHEN
1124 N. HACIENDA BLVD, LA PUENTE, CA

DR. JOHN SILK
23151 VERDUGO DR., STE. 107, LAGUNA HILLS, CA

DR. DAVID A. STEENBLOCK
22706 ASPAN ST., STE. 500, LAKE FOREST, CA

DR. MICHAEL J. GROSSMAN
24432 MUIRLANDS BLVD., LAKE FOREST, CA

DR. CHARLES GABELMAN
24491 JUTEWOOD PL., LAKE FOREST, CA

DR. PRADEEP DAMLE
1600 W. AVENUE J, LANCASTER, CA

DR. IFEOMA IKENZE
5 BON AIR RD., STE. 220, LARKSPUR, CA

DR. EUGENE D. FINKLE
P.O. BOX 309, LAYTONVILLE, CA

INSTITUTE OF HEALTH
6970 CENTRAL AVE., LEMON GROVE, CA

DR. GERALDINE DONALDSON
1074 MURRIETA BLVD., LIVERMORE, CA

DR. CLYDE D. HAWLEY
1038 MURRIETA BLVD., LIVERMORE, CA

DR. ADAM DEL TORTO JR
4277 SIRIUS AVE., LOMPOC, CA

DR. ROBERT GREEN
2756 PALO VERDE AVE., LONG BEACH, CA

DR. TIMOTHY E. PARKER
P.O. BOX 1428, LONG BEACH, CA

DR. STEPHEN E. BROWN
P.O. BOX 1428, LONG BEACH, CA

DR. CLAUDE MARQUETTE
5050 EL CAMINO REAL, STE. 110, LOS ALTOS, CA

DR. ROBERT F. CATHCART, III
127 2ND ST., STE. 4, LOS ALTOS, CA

DR. JACK LOSKIU
1333 S. GENESEE AVE., LOS ANGELES, CA

DR. G. M. SHIELDS
314 N. HARPER AVE., LOS ANGELES, CA

DR. SORAM KHALSA
8631 W. 3RD ST., STE. 1135E, LOS ANGELES, CA

DR. EMMANUEL MOJTAHEDIAN
6425 WHITTIER BLVD., LOS ANGELES, CA

DR. FRISCA YAN-GO
710 WESTWOOD PLAZA, LOS ANGELES, CA

DR. NACHMAN BRAUTBAR
2222 OCEAN VIEW AVE., #100, LOS ANGELES, CA

DR. JAMES J. JULLIAN
1654 N. CAHUENGA BLVD., LOS ANGELES, CA

DR. RANDY W. MARTIN
2211 CORINTH AVE., STE. 204, LOS ANGELES, CA

DR. JOAN PRIESTLEY
7080 HOLLYWOOD BLVD., STE. 603, LOS ANGELES, CA

DR. MICHAEL GALITZER
12381 WILSHIRE BLVD., LOS ANGELES, CA

DR. M. JAHANGIRL
2156 S. SANTA FE AVE., LOS ANGELES, CA

DR. IAN MUSSMAN
1320 MILLER DR., APT. 12, LOS ANGELES, CA

DR. LASZLO I. BELENYESSY
12732 W. WASHINGTON BLVD., #D, LOS ANGELES, CA

DR. CARL GROOMS
3904 TIVOLI AVE., LOS ANGELES, CA

DR. CATHLEEN M. RAPP
451 LOS GATOS BLVD., STE. 204, LOS GATOS, CA

DR. R. O. WAITON
221 ALMENDRA AVE., LOS GATOS, CA

DR. JANET ZAND
P.O. BOX 4144, MALIBU, CA

DR. SANDRA NYSTROM
500 S. SEPULVEDA BLVD., STE. 106, MANHATTAN BEACH, CA

DR. VINCENT MARINKOVICH
90 MIDDLEFIELD RD., MENLO PARK, CA

DR. PETER PAULAY
103 GILBERT AVE., MENLO PARK, CA

DR. MARTIN L. ROSSMAN
1 WILLOW ST., #4, MILL VALLEY, CA

DR. ELLEN DECK
115 ELINOR AVE., MILL VALLEY, CA

DR. LARRIE GOLDSMITH
447 MILLER AVE., MILL VALLEY, CA

DR. JONATHAN SHORE
316 MILLER AVE., MILL VALLEY, CA

DR. ELLIOTT R. PHILLIPS
11550 INDIAN HILLS RD., #291, MISSION HILLS, CA

DR. JON F. SASSIN
P.O. BOX 7999, MISSION HILLS, CA

DR. DONALD R. WHITAKER
26302 LA PAZ RD., STE. 207, MISSION VIEJO, CA

DR. LON B. WORK
841 FOAM ST., STE. D, MONTEREY, CA

DR. STEPHEN L. ODELL
625 MAIN ST., MORRO BAY, CA

DR. CARL EBNOTHER
759 VILLA ST., MOUNTAIN VIEW, CA

DR. STEPHEN BANNISTER
119 ARGALL WAY, NEVADA CITY, CA

DR. LESTER G. ROSE
P.O. BOX 1566, NEVADA CITY, CA

DR. PAUL A. SELECKY
301 N. NEWPORT BLVD., NEWPORT BEACH, CA

DR. JULIAN WHITAKER
4321 BIRCH ST., STE. 100, NEWPORT BEACH, CA

DR. BONNIE ROTHEISER
16706 GLEDHILL ST., NORTH HILLS, CA

DR. LAUREN SCHMITZ
4924 VINELAND AVE., NORTH HOLLYWOOD, CA

DR. JEREMY COLE
18300 ROSCOE BLVD., NORTHRIDGE, CA

DR. MORTIMER WEISS
65 BOGEY LN., NOVATO, CA

DR. LISA STERNLIEB
230 GRAND AVE., OAKLAND, CA

DR. EDWARD SPENCER
481 MERRITT AVE., OAKLAND, CA

DR. ELISA SHARPS
600 GRAND AVE., STE. 308, OAKLAND, CA

DR. MARY J. LUCK
407 ORANGE ST., OAKLAND, CA

DR. KEITH STETSON
484 LAKE PARK AVE., #343, OAKLAND, CA

DR. RICHARD NUSSR
3100 SUMMIT ST., OAKLAND, CA

DR. REBECCA WILLIAMS
3012 HARRISON ST., OAKLAND, CA

DR. JANET KNIVETON
5311 COLLEGE AVE., OAKLAND, CA

DR. JERROLD A. KRAM
3100 SUMMIT ST., OAKLAND, CA

DR. LORETTA EARLY
4100 35TH AVE., OAKLAND, CA

DR. JAI J. NOIRE
2924 CALIFORNIA ST., OAKLAND, CA

DR. GENEVA WHITAKER
649 58TH ST., OAKLAND, CA

DR. JONICE M. OWEN
400 40TH ST., STE. 202, OAKLAND, CA

DR. ALICE HIATT
26 CHICO CT., OAKLAND, CA

DR. BETH MARX
546 WELDON AVE., OAKLAND, CA

DR. FRANK CHUNG
5664 BROADWAY, OAKLAND, CA

DR. RICHARD HILTNER
169 E. EL ROBLAR DR., OJAI, CA

DR. SARAH MOSKO
1100 W. STEWART DR., ORANGE, CA

DR. ROBERT PRESTON
P.O. BOX 4125, OROVILLE, CA

DR. MOHAMED MOHARRAM
300 W. 5TH ST., STE. B, OXNARD, CA

DR. F. P. McBROOM
1515 PALISADES DR., STE. P, PACIFIC PALISADES, CA

DR. SCOTT GREGORY
P.O. BOX 1445, PACIFIC PALISADES, CA

DR. HYLA CASS
1608 MICHAEL LN., PACIFIC PALISADES, CA

DR. BRIAN REES
17308 W. SUNSET BLVD., PACIFIC PALISADES, CA

DR. HENRY PASTERNAK
526 PALISADES DR., PACIFIC PALISADES, CA

DR. LEXI FISHER
2825 E. TAHQUITZ CANYON WAY, PALM SPRINGS, CA

DR. FRANK BERLIN
1240 E. AVENUE S., APT. 281, PALMDALE, CA

DR. CHRISTINE GREEN
145 N. CALIFORNIA AVE., PALO ALTO, CA

DR. WILLIAM J. SAYER
P.O. BOX 60688, PALO ALTO, CA

DR. ROBERT S. EISENBERG
P.O. BOX 7, PASADENA, CA

DR. GABRIEL COUSINS
200 SPRING HILL RD., PETALUMA, CA

DR. BRYAN BOUCH
245 KENTUCKY ST., STE. A, PETALUMA, CA

DR. WILLIAM PRANGE
245 KENTUCKY ST., #A, PETALUMA, CA

DR. TIMOTHY KUSS
2242 MORELLO AVE., PLEASANT HILL, CA

DR. DENNIS NICHOLSON
1798 N. GAREY AVE., POMONA, CA

DR. FARES ELGHAZI
1798 N. GAREY AVE., POMONA, CA

DR. JOHN B. PARK
250 N. G ST., PORTERVILLE, CA

DR. JEFF MERSKY
15 COMMERCIAL ST., PORTOLA, CA

DR. BRUCE WALKER
P.O. BOX 1080, QUINCY, CA

DR. R. PETERS
2551 PARK MARINA DR., STE. 1, REDDING, CA

DR. BESSIE J. TILLMAN
2054 MARKET ST., REDDING, CA

DR. PETER STERN
P.O. BOX 769, REDWAY, CA

DR. GLENN W. SHORT
179 HUDSON ST., REDWOOD CITY, CA

DR. BERNHARD VOTTERI
170 ALAMEDA, REDWOOD CITY, CA

DR. ROBERT N. PAVY
170 ALAMEDA, REDWOOD CITY, CA

DR. ILONA ABRAHAM
19231 VICTORY BLVD., RESEDA, CA

DR. JOE MCSWEYN
19231 VICTORY BLVD., STE. 151, RESEDA, CA

DR. CHRISTINE BECKER
1812 CARLSON BLVD., RICHMOND, CA

DR. CHARLENE LEUNG
6016 ORCHARD AVE., RICHMOND, CA

DR. HITEN SHAW
6117 BROCKTON AVE., STE. 104, RIVERSIDE, CA

DR. JEFFREY R. SIMONS
4445 MAGNOLIA AVE, RIVERSIDE, CA

DR. LOUIS LINGREN
3816 12TH ST., RIVERSIDE, CA

DR. CARL NELLEY
4240 ROCKLIN RD., STE. 1, ROCKLIN, CA

DR. SUNILA PERERA
404 SUNRISE AVE., ROSEVILLE, CA

DR. JAMES R. MALLY
112 DOUGLAS BLVD., ROSEVILLE, CA

DR. LYDIA WYTRZES
650 HOWE AVE., STE. 910, SACRAMENTO, CA

DR. J. G. STROUP
1817 PROFESSIONAL DR., SACRAMENTO, CA

DR. JOAN REYNOLDS
3001 J ST., #100, SACRAMENTO, CA

DR. PAUL ASAHARA
4410 24TH ST., SACRAMENTO, CA

DR. MICHAEL KWIKER
3301 ALTA ARDEN EXPY., STE. 3, SACRAMENTO, CA

DR. NONY MORGAN
1150 MAIN ST., #1, SAINT HELENA, CA

DR. CONNIE MARTIN
1317 CRESTVIEW DR., SAN CARLOS, CA

DR. DOROTHY V. CALABRESE
655 CAMINO DE LOS MARES, SAN CLEMENTE, CA

DR. WILLIAM DOELL
971 CALLE NEGOCIO, SAN CLEMENTE, CA

DR. GERONIMO RUBIO
555 SATURN BLVD., STE. B, SAN DIEGO, CA

OKTURO CENTRO MEDICO
P.O. BOX 430713, SAN DIEGO, CA

DR. BERNARD RIMLAND
4182 ADAMS AVE., SAN DIEGO, CA

DR. HENRY FUSCO
2611 DENVER ST., SAN DIEGO, CA

DR. ROBERT PRICE
1729 COLLINGWOOD DR., SAN DIEGO, CA

ST LUKES HOSPITAL
405 W. WASHINGTON ST., SAN DIEGO, CA

DR. TIMOTHY R. DOOLEY
4095 JACKDAW ST., SAN DIEGO, CA

DR. LUCIEN JASSY
4077 5TH AVE. BLDG., SAN DIEGO, CA

DR. LAWRENCE TAYLOR
3330 3RD AVE., STE. 402, SAN DIEGO, CA

LIVINGSTON FOUNDATION MEDICAL CENTER
3232 DUKE ST., SAN DIEGO, CA

DR. MILTON MILLMAN
2602 1ST AVE. #6104, SAN DIEGO, CA

DR. RENATA SHAFOR
1842 3RD AVE., SAN DIEGO, CA

DR. ZANE R. GARD
P.O. BOX 231309, SAN DIEGO, CA

DR. MARK LANGER
3223 WEBSTER ST., SAN FRANCISCO, CA

DR. MAUREEN C. HICKS
829 HEAD ST., SAN FRANCISCO, CA

DR. LEO BAKKER
830 FELTON ST., SAN FRANCISCO, CA

DR. DENISE R. MARK
345 W. PORTAL AVE., SAN FRANCISCO, CA

DR. ELIOTT S. BLACKMAN
1956 UNION ST., SAN FRANCISCO, CA

DR. MARISYA BRZYSKI
133 MAGNOLIA ST., SAN FRANCISCO, CA

DR. MICHAEL CARPENDALE
4150 CLEMENT ST., SAN FRANCISCO, CA

DR. PHILIP BROOKS
575 9TH AVE., SAN FRANCISCO, CA

DR. ERIKA GOOD
3801 SACRAMENTO ST., #100, SAN FRANCISCO, CA

DR. SHIRLEY SCOTT
3698 CALIFORNIA ST., SAN FRANCISCO, CA

DR. MARIANNE LONERGAN
1427 BALBOA ST., SAN FRANCISCO, CA

DR. COREY W. WEINSTEIN
1109 VICENTE ST., #104, SAN FRANCISCO, CA

DR. PAUL LYNN
345 W. PORTAL AVE., SAN FRANCISCO, CA

DR. KSTRINA L. COOMBS
3885 18TH ST., SAN FRANCISCO, CA

DR. RICHARD KUNIN
2698 PACIFIC AVE., SAN FRANCISCO, CA

DR. ALAN S. LEVINE
20 EAGLE ST., SAN FRANCISCO, CA

DR. LAU KOON-HUNG
1333 PACIFIC AVE., STE. E, SAN FRANCISCO, CA

DR. DAVID FIELD
1201 NOE ST., #25, SAN FRANCISCO, CA

Dk. ANN HONIGMAN
1500 SANSOME ST., #103, SAN FRANCISCO, CA

DR. JOHN C. ETCHEVERRY
2 CONNECTICUT ST., SAN FRANCISCO, CA

DR. STEVE VACCARO
426 ELIZABETH ST., SAN FRANCISCO, CA

DR. KATHLEEN MOORE
220 BUSH ST., STE. 450, SAN FRANCISCO, CA

DR. ROBERT J. SINAIKO
450 SUTTER ST., RM. 1124, SAN FRANCISCO, CA

DR. DELORES HEPBURN
80 CANYON DR., SAN FRANCISCO, CA

DR. CARL HANGEE-BAUER
862 FOLSOM ST., SAN FRANCISCO, CA

DR. SYDNEY C. CHOSLOVSKY
675 E. SANTA CLARA ST., SAN JOSE, CA

DR. RICHARD TREVINO
280 N. JACKSON AVE., STE. C, SAN JOSE, CA

DR. MARGO BELLAMY
1210 GARBO WAY, APT. 1, SAN JOSE, CA

DR. VIRGINIA HANDLY
2021 THE ALAMEDA, STE. 170, SAN JOSE, CA

DR. W. S. CONNOR
675 E. SANTA CLARA ST., SAN JOSE, CA

DR. STEVEN H. GEE
595 ESTUDILLO AVE., SAN LEANDRO, CA

DR. WILLIAM C. KUBITSCHEK
1194 CALLE MARIA, SAN MARCOS, CA

DR. F. T. GUILFORD
101 S. SAN MATEO DR., STE. 303, SAN MATEO, CA

DR. ROSS B. GORDON
4144 REDWOOD HWY., SAN RAFAEL, CA

DR. SANDRA B. GOLUBINSKI
P.O. BOX 2203, SAN RAFAEL, CA

DR. ROBERT HASKILL
12 AQUA VISTA DR., SAN RAFAEL CA

DR. ELSON HAAS
25 MITCHELL BLVD., STE. 8, SAN RAFAEL, CA

DR. RON MIKLEBOST
9260 ALCOSTA BLVD., SAN RAMON, CA

DR. BETTY STRATFORD
1501 BOLLINGER CANYON RD., SAN RAMON, CA

DR. WOLFRAM KUHNAU
P.O. BOX 432014, SAN YSIDRO, CA

CYDEL CLINIC
P.O. BOX 434290, SAN YSIDRO, CA

DR. HENRY YUN
2036 DAIRY MART RD., STE. 122, SAN YSIDRO, CA

DR. GUSTAVO A. DEL CID
2630 E. BEYER BLVD., #496, SAN YSIDRO, CA

DR. ROBERT B. GOLD
1905 COLLEGE AVE., STE. B2, SANTA ANA, CA

DR. RONALD WEMPEN
3620 S. BRISTOL ST., STE. 306, SANTA ANA, CA

DR. HUMBERTO FLORIAN
1311 N. BROADWAY, #C, SANTA ANA, CA

DR. GARY W. EMERSON
1125 E. 17TH ST., STE. N-161, SANTA ANA, CA

DR. H. J. HOEGERMAN
101 W. ARRELLAGA ST., STE. D, SANTA BARBARA, CA

DR. BRUCE DAVIS
530 E. MICHELTORENA ST., SANTA BARBARA, CA

DR. ANANDA ZAREN
28 E. CANON PERDIDO ST., SANTA BARBARA, CA

DR. KATHRYN JACOBSON
300 E. CANON PERDIDO ST., #E1, SANTA BARBARA, CA

DR. BAMBI MERRYWEATHER
P.O. BOX 5573, SANTA BARBARA, CA

DR. DAVID DONER
2410 FLETCHER AVE., STE. 301, SANTA BARBARA, CA

DR. JOHN DAWSON JR
2958 STATE ST., SANTA BARBARA, CA

DR. JOHN ACKETMAN
2417 CASTILLO ST., SANTA BARBARA, CA

DR. PHILIP G. NEWELL
1642 CALLE CANON, SANTA BARBARA, CA

DR. DORALEE WAADT
1187 COAST VILLAGE RD., #1-174, SANTA BARBARA, CA

DR. CATHERINE MORRIS
626 FREDERICK ST., SANTA CRUZ, CA

DR. MARK SCHWARTZ
1658 SOQUEL DR., SANTA CRUZ, CA

DR. DENISE WILSON
P.O. BOX 7129, SANTA CRUZ, CA

DR. DONALD S. RICH
706 WESTERN DR., SANTA CRUZ, CA

DR. MICHAEL TIERRA
912 CENTER ST., SANTA CRUZ, CA

DR. WAYNE MILLER
2441 PROFESSIONAL PKY., SANTA MARIA, CA

DR. ANNA JALAS
523 E. CYPRESS ST., SANTA MARIA, CA

DR. ROBERT C. MILLER
109 W. FESLER ST., SANTA MARIA, CA

DR. SKIP SHODEN
429 SANTA MONICA BLVD., #350, SANTA MONICA, CA

DR. JIM BLECHMAN
1137 2ND ST., STE 110, SANTA MONICA, CA

DR. ERIC J. DOLGIN
2210 WILSHIRE BLVD., #281, SANTA MONICA, CA

DR. PAMELA DURGIN
612 SANTA MONICA BLVD., SANTA MONICA, CA

DR. MURRAY R. SUSSER
2730 WILSHIRE BLVD., STE. 110, SANTA MONICA, CA

DR. MICHAEL ROSENBAUM
2730 WILSHIRE BLVD., STE. 110, SANTA MONICA, CA

DR. J. C. GREEN
850 3RD ST., STE. C, SANTA ROSA, CA

DR. MICHAEL DOLAN
2729 YULUPA AVE., SANTA ROSA, CA

DR. TERRI SU
1038 4TH ST. STE. 3, SANTA ROSA, CA

DR. MICHAEL G. CARLSTON
1154 MONTGOMERY DR., STE. 5, SANTA ROSA, CA

DR. SANDRA N. KAMIAK
14567 BIG BASIN WAY, SARATOGA, CA

DR. HELENE SILVER
34 GATE 5 RD., SAUSALITO, CA

DR. RICHARD EHRET
301 HARBOR DR., SAUSALITO, CA

DR. TERESA LUCCHESI-COOK
5437 SCOTTS VALLEY DR., SCOTTS VALLEY, CA

DR. DIAN WAGNER
868 GRAVENSTEIN HWY. N, SEBASTOPOL, CA

DR. DENNIS L. VOSSEN
460 PITT AVE., SEBASTOPOL, CA

DR. PETER MADILL
7005 HAZEL COTTER CT., SEBASTOPOL, CA

DR. CLIFFORD FRASER
4910 VAN NUYS BLVD., STE. 110, SHERMAN OAKS, CA

DR. JAMES D. SCHULLER
P.O. BOX 297, SMITH RIVER, CA

DR. ARTHUR KASLOW
795 ALAMO PINTADO RD., SOLVANG, CA

DR. JAMES H. ADAMS
101 ANDRIEUX ST., SONOMA, CA

DR. JEFFREY JOHNSON
169 S. SHEPHERD ST., SONORA, CA

DR. MARY B. ANDERSON
3015 PORTER ST., SOQUEL, CA

DR. STEVEN D. STEWART
4841 SOQUEL DR., SOQUEL, CA

DR. WILLIAM J. GOLDWAG
7499 CERRITOS AVE., STANTON, CA

DR. CHARLES E. LAW
3959 LAUREL CANYON BL., STE. 1, STUDIO CITY, CA

DR. HARRY F. SWOPE
12522 MOORPARK ST., STE. 108, STUDIO CITY, CA

DR. FRANK GRADILLAS
26010 McCALL BLVD., STE. B, SUN CITY, CA

DR. BRIAN MILLER
10323 NEWHOME AVE., SUNLAND, CA

DR. JOHN WAKEFIELD
970 W. EL CAMINO REAL, SUNNYVALE, CA

DR. STEVEN M. KATZ
19100 VENTURA BLVD., STE. P, TARZANA, CA

DR. MELVYN MERBACH
4751 VIVIANA DR., TARZANA, CA

DR. RICHARD A. HENDRICKS
1050 LAS TABLAS RD., TEMPLETON, CA

DR. RONALD A. POPPER
2230 LYNN RD., THOUSAND OAKS, CA

DR. GUNNAR HEUSE
323 S. MOORPARK RD., THOUSAND OAKS, CA

DR. PHILLIP H. TAYLOR
325 S. MOORPARK RD., THOUSAND OAKS, CA

DR. ANITA MILLEN
1010 CRENSHAW BLVD., STE. 170, TORRANCE, CA

DR. LAWRENCE W. KNEISLEY
3330 LOMITA BLVD., TORRANCE, CA

DR. WOODROW WEISS
3661 TORRANCE BLVD., TORRANCE, CA

DR. DAVID WONG
3250 LOMITA BLVD., STE. 209, TORRANCE, CA

DR. JENNY SAKAMOTO
23441 MADISON ST. S., STE 215, TORRANCE CA

DR. NANCY SARRAT
P.O. BOX 3390, TRUCKEE, CA

DR. ANNIE POLUCHA
P.O. BOX 8954, TRUCKEE, CA

DR. WINSTON A. BOLER
3418 SONOMA BLVD., VALLEJO, CA

DR. ROBERT SIMS
710 TENNESSEE ST., VALLEJO, CA

DR. SANTIAGO CARIN
712 NEBRASKA ST., VALLEJO, CA

DR. DOUGLAS SLATER
845 REDWOOD ST., VALLEJO, CA

DR. LINDA C. JOHNSTON
7549 LOUISE AVE., VAN NUYS, CA

DR. PATRICIA TEMPLE
620 E. THOMPSON BLVD., VENTURA, CA

DR. JAMES W. COLQUITT
10883 TELEGRAPH RD., VENTURA, CA

DR. EDWARD SIVAS
14270 7TH ST., STE. 5-146, VICTORVILLE, CA

DR. WILLIAM R. WINN
400 W. MINERAL KING AVE., VISALIA, CA

DR. ALAN S. CHARLES
1414 MARIA LN., WALNUT CREEK, CA

DR. MARION MAYNARD
1844 SAN MIGUEL DR., WALNUT CREEK, CA

DR. HOWARD B. SCHNEIDER
1874 BONANZA ST., STE. A, WALNUT CREEK, CA

DR. JEFF LESTER
135 MONTE VISTA AVE., WATSONVILLE, CA

DR. WILLIAM HEMBY
P.O. BOX 901, WEIMAR, CA

DR. GORDON DOWDS
23101 SHERMAN PL., STE. 108, WEST HILLS, CA

DR. ELIZABETH SCHENKEL
23101 SHERMAN PL., STE. 108, WEST HILLS, CA

DR. WALTON V. STUART
P.O. BOX 628, WEST POINT, CA

DR. PHILLIS HICKMAN
P,O. BOX 788, WINDSOR, CA

DR. ALEXANDER SINAVSKY
22381 ALGUNAS RD., WOODLAND HILLS, CA

DR. DAN WILSON
6081 CALLE MIRADOR, YORBA LINDA, CA

DR. THOMAS McCLASKEY
2420 BLEVIN RD., YUBA CITY, CA

DR. MARITA NEISS
49058 QUAIL BUSH RD., YUCCA VALLEY, CA

COLORADO

DR. HAROLD C. WHITCOMB, JR.
100 E. MAIN ST., STE. 201, ASPEN, CO

DR. CHARLES K. KIMMEL
12369 E. CORNELL AVE., #B, AURORA, CO

DR. RICHARD W. WALSH
14652 E. 2ND AVE., #206, AURORA, CO

DR. JODY K. SHEVINS
2880 FOLSOM ST., #210A, BOULDER, CO

DR. LINDA WRIGHT
3980 BROADWAY ST., STE. 202, BOULDER, CO

DR. JOHANNAH REILLY
2660 13TH ST., BOULDER, CO

DR. S. C. DUHON
4841 ELDORADO SPRINGS DR., BOULDER, CO

DR. BONNIE ALEXANDRA
1011 BROADWAY ST., BOULDER, CO

DR. CHARLES M. CROPLEY
2885 AURORA AVE., STE. 19, BOULDER, CO

DR. ANDREW LANGE
3122 8TH ST., BOULDER, CO

DR. GEORGE JUETERSONKE
5455 N. UNION BLVD., STE. 200, COLORADO SPRINGS, CO

DR. BARBARA SHEARS
1023 N. WEBER ST., COLORADO SPRINGS, CO

DR. RUTH ADELE
1625 W. UINTAH ST., STE. I, COLORADO SPRINGS, CO

DR. SANDRA C. DENTON
5080 LIST DR., COLORADO SPRINGS, CO

DR. JAMES R. FISH
3030 N. HANCOCK AVE., COLORADO SPRINGS, CO

DR. HAL A. HUGGINS
5080 LIST DR., COLORADO SPRINGS, CO

DR. KENDALL A. GERDES
1617 VINE ST., DENVER, CO

DR. JEAN ROWE
3355 S. FLOWER ST., APT. 151, DENVER, CO

DR. RENA BLOOM
161 MADISON ST., DENVER, CO

DR. EDWARD SHAPIRO
201 UNIVERSITY BLVD., STE. 203, DENVER, CO

DR. MARK SHUSTERMAN
3443 S. GALENA ST., STE. 210, DENVER, CO

DR. JACOB J. SCHOR
161 MADISON ST., DENVER, CO

DR. NICHOLAS J. NOSSAMAN
1750 HIGH ST., DENVER, CO

DR. TOM RAVIN
45 S. DAHLIA ST., DENVER, CO

DR. CHRISTOPHR HUSSAR
2222 E. 18TH AVE., DENVER, CO

DR. DENNIS H. KAY
6053 S. QUEBEC ST., STE. 202, ENGLEWOOD, CO

DR. DANIEL LAMAR
819 LOCUST CT., FORT COLLINS, CO

DR. MELVIN KALLSEN
316 MEEKER ST., FORT MORGAN, CO

DR. SUSAN C. ALLEN
P.O. BOX 2227, FRISCO, CO

DR. BARRY FIELDS
1905 BLAKE AVE., GLENWOOD SPRINGS, CO

DR. ELLEN W. DALE
25170 MONTANE DR. W., GOLDEN, CO

DR. NITA A. WOLF
350 INDIANA ST., STE. 610, GOLDEN, CO

DR. GAIL KUETTEL
929 38TH AVENUE CT., STE. 104, GREELEY, CO

DR. CHERYL A. KOS
3722 W. ROSEWALK CT., HIGHLANDS RANCH, CO

DR. BONNIE STARK
10576 W. ALAMEDA AVE., LAKEWOOD, CO

DR. BONNIE ALEXANDRA
10576 W. ALAMEDA AVE., LAKEWOOD, CO

DR. ZACHARY BRINKERHOFF
7063 W. COLFAX AVE., LAKEWOOD, CO

DR. LINDA C. WRIGHT
421 21ST AVE., STE. 7, LONGMONT, CO

DR. KEITH LUNDBERG
25 S. SELIG AVE., MONTROSE, CO

DR. R. C. CUNNINGHAM
P.O. BOX 632, PENROSE, CO

DR. ROB KRAKOVITZ
94 ELK RANGE DR., SNOWMASS, CO

CONNECTICUT

DR. PAUL G. RATHE
332 RIVERSVILLE RD., GREENWICH, CT

DR. GABRIELE KALLENBORB
54 LAFAYETTE PL., GREENWICH, CT

DR. AHMED N. CURRIM
148 EAST AVE., NORWALK, CT

DR. PAUL G. EPSTEIN
9 BERKELEY ST., NORWALK, CT

DR. MARSHALL MANDELL
P.O. BOX 2072, NORWALK, CT

DR. MARVIN P. SCHWEITZER
71 EAST AVE., STE. F, NORWALK, CT

DR. RONALD A. GRANT
P.O. BOX 1174, WESTON, CT

DR. HERRICK P. GOODMAN
21 TRAILS END RD., WESTON, CT

DR. HOWARD FINE
468 MAIN ST., WESTPORT, CT

DR. RONALD SCHMID
39 RICHMONDVILLE AVE., WESTPORT, CT

DR. LAWRENCE J. CAPRIO
830 POST RD. E., WESTPORT, CT

DR. RAJESH P. VYAS
299 GREENS FARMS RD., WESTPORT, CT

DR. JOHN McMAHON
157 OLD RIDGEFIELD RD., WILTON, CT

DR. DEIRDRE WILLIAMS
157 OLD RIDGEFIELD RD., WILTON, CT

DELAWARE

DR. EUGENE GODFREY
100 SKULL TER., DOVER, DE

DR. ROGER ALLEN
33 GLENEAGLES CT., DOVER, DE

DR. JEROME E. GROLL
421 SAVANNAH RD., LEWES, DE

DR. DAVID EHRENFELD
710 GREENBANK RD., WILMINGTON, DE

DR. KENNETH E. DE GROOT
1401 SILVERSIDE RD., WILMINGTON, DE

DR. DIANE NEWMAN
509 S. CLAYTON ST., WILMINGTON, DE

DR. ROBERT H. HALL
1509 GILPIN AVE., WILMINGTON, DE

DR. MITCHEL E. SHAPIRO
1207 DELAWARE AVE., WILMINGTON, DE

DISTRICT OF COLUMBIA

DR. IOANA A. RAZI
3537 R. ST. N.W., WASHINGTON, DC

DR. SAMUEL J. POTOLICCHIO, JR.
3800 RESERVOIR RD. N.W., WASHINGTON, DC

DR. PAUL BEALS
2639 CONNECTICUT AVE. N.W., WASHINGTON, DC

DR. DIETMAR SCHILDWAECHTER
P.O. BOX 17602, WASHINGTON, DC

DR. NANCY LONSDORF
4910 MASSACHUSETTS AVE. N.W., WASHINGTON, DC

DR. D. W. HARRISON
910 KENNEDY ST. N.W., WASHINGTON, DC

DR. ANDREA D. SULLIVAN
4601 CONNECTICUT AVE. N.W., WASHINGTON, DC

FLORIDA

DR. JOYA SCHOEN
701 E. ALTAMONTE DR., #304, ALTAMONTE SPRINGS, FL

DR. LOIS CROWLEY
162 S. POLK AVE., ARCADIA, FL

DR. RICHARD WORSHAM
303 1ST ST., ATLANTIC BEACH, FL

DR. NORMAN T. GIBSON
104 S.W. 5TH ST., STE. 2, BELLE GLADE, FL

DR. MARK J. RUDERMAN
7100 W. CAMINO REAL., STE. 402, BOCA RATON, FL

DR. ALBERT F. ROBBINS
400 S. DIXIE HWY., STE. 210, BOCA RATON, FL

DR. NEIL C. HENDERSON
30 S.E. 7TH ST., BOCA RATON, FL

DR. BRUCE HEDENDAL
301 CRAWFORD BLVD., BOCA RATON, FL

DR. SHEILA R. SHAFER
899 MEADOWS RD., STE. 101, BOCA RATON, FL

DR. LEONARD HAIMES
7300 N. FEDERAL HWY., STE. 107, BOCA RATON, FL

DR. ETERI MELNIKOV
116 MANATEE AVE. E., BRADENTON, FL

DR. GEOFFREY DEVINE
13061 CORTEZ BLVD., BROOKSVILLE, FL

DR. JAMES PARSONS
707 MULLETT RD., STE. 110, CAPE CANAVERAL, FL

DR. HARRISON E. ELLIS
228 BRIGHTON WAY, CASSELBERRY, FL

DR. CHARLES FLEMING
1831 N. BELCHER RD., STE. C1, CLEARWATER, FL

DR. HARRIET M. D'COSTA
1481 BELLEAIR RD., CLEARWATER, FL

DR. L. E. ZIMMERMAN
277 W. COCOA BEACH CSWY., COCOA BEACH, FL

DR. AZAEL BORROMEO
20 N.E. 3RD ST., CRYSTAL RIVER, FL

DR. FREDERICK C. BRICKLE
730 DUNLAWTON AVE., DAYTONA BEACH, FL

DR. W. R. RUNDLES
5795 TAYLOR BRANCH RD., DAYTONA BEACH, FL

DR. MARJO D. SEGLER
2915 S. FEDERAL HWY., #D-1, DELRAY BEACH, FL

DR. STEFANO DIMAURO
1333 S. STATE ROAD 7, FORT LAUDERDALE, FL

DR. BRUCE DOOLEY
1493 S.E. 17TH ST., FORT LAUDERDALE, FL

DR. GLENN R. SINGER
1600 S. ANDREWS AVE., FORT LAUDERDALE, FL

DR. HERBERT R. SLAVIN
7200 W. COMMERCIAL BLVD., FORT LAUDERDALE, FL

DR. L. E. GOLDMAN
1451 N.W. 62ND ST., FORT LAUDERDALE, FL

DR. ROBI ROSENFELD
6560 KESTREL CIR., FORT MYERS, FL

DR. GARY L. PYNCKEL
3940 METRO PKY., STE. 115, FORT MYERS, FL

DR. RANDALL A. LANGSTON
1005 MAR WALT DR., FORT WALTON BEACH, FL

DR. MARTIN BRODY
7100 W. 20TH AVE., HIALEAH, FL

DR. ERNEST E. KELL
1420 S. 20TH AVE., HOLLYWOOD, FL

DR. HERBERT PARDELL
210 S. FEDERAL HWY., STE. 302, HOLLYWOOD, FL

DR. CARLOS F. GONZALEZ
7991 S. SUNCOAST BLVD., HOMOSASSA, FL

DR. JEFFREY MARCUS
3733 E. GULF TO LAKE HWY., INVERNESS, FL

DR. SANDFORD POLLAK
9765 SAN JOSE BLVD., STE. 105, JACKSONVILLE, FL

DR. HENRY N. MERRITT
6037 LONGCHAMP DR., JACKSONVILLE, FL

DR. CYRUS A. WOOD
5627 ATLANTIC BLVD., STE. 2, JACKSONVILLE, FL

DR. JOSEPH KAPLAN
4500 SAN PABLO RD. S., JACKSONVILLE, FL

DR. DENNIS J. MCDONAGH
P.O. BOX 2982, JACKSONVILLE, FL

DR. ALLAN SPREEN
5627 ATLANTIC BLVD., STE. 2, JACKSONVILLE, FL

DR. PAUL FREDRICKSON
4500 SAN PABLO RD. S., JACKSONVILLE, FL

DR. LAWRENCE SMOLLEY
800 PRUDENTIAL DR., JACKSONVILLE, FL

DR. DAVID ROSE
117 W. 6TH ST., JACKSONVILLE, FL

DR. EDWARD ALTMAN
6390 W. INDIANTOWN RD., JUPITER, FL

DR. NEIL A. AHNER
1080 E. INDIANTOWN RD., JUPITER, FL

DR. ED J. GENDERSKI
240 GALEN DR., APT. 305, KEY BISCAYNE, FL

DR. PHILIP K. PARSONS
P.O. BOX 266, KEYSTONE HEIGHTS, FL

DR. DALE BARNES
316 CHURCH ST., KISSIMMEE, FL

DR. JAMES THOMAS
440 LAKE PEARL DR., LAKE HELEN, FL

DR. J. A. TANKERSLEY
4175 S. CONGRESS AVE., STE. E, LAKE WORTH, FL

DR. CHARLES VICKERS
4325 HIGHLAND PARK BLVD., LAKELAND, FL

DR. C. G. CHEATWOOD
3540 S. FLORIDA AVE., LAKELAND, FL

DR. EBERTO PINEIRO
1600 LAKELAND HILLS BLVD., LAKELAND, FL

DR. JOSEPH A. GOTZL
16528 FLORIDA AVE., LUTZ, FL

DR. J. L. ALEXANDER
1100 S ORLANDO AVE., MAITLAND, FL

PROFESSIONAL HEALTH ASSOCIATES
175 LOOKOUT PL., #101, MAITLAND, FL

DR. JOYA L. SCHOEN
341 N. MAITLAND AVE., STE. 200, MAITLAND, FL

DR. GEORGE J. SCHERER
2115 WAVERLY PL., MELBOURNE, FL

DR. JAY GUTIERREZ
514 LOVERIDGE DR., MELBOURNE, FL

DR. DENNIS K. KING
1401 S. APOLLO BLVD., MELBOURNE, FL

DR. MARCEL J. DERAY
6125 S.W. 31ST ST., MIAMI, FL

DR. ALAN J. SERRINS
7400 N. KENDALL DR., MIAMI, FL

DR. STANLEY J. CANNON
9085 S.W. 87TH AVE., MIAMI, FL

DR. BERNARD J. LETOURNEAU
6475 S.W. 40TH ST., MIAMI, FL

DR. GARY SHULL
1001 IVES DAIRY RD., STE. 202, MIAMI, FL

DR. HOBART T. FELDMAN
16800 N.W. 2ND AVE., STE. 301, MIAMI, FL

DR. JOSEPH G. GODOROV
9055 S.W. 87TH AVE., STE. 307, MIAMI, FL

DR. SANFORD COHEN
17891 S. DIXIE HWY., MIAMI, FL

DR. LENORE ANOLICK
11241 S.W. 114TH LANE CIR., MIAMI, FL

DR. EMANUEL ORFAS
12811 S.W. 149TH ST, MIAMI, FL

DR. ROBERT R. KARMAN
253 S.W. 8TH ST., MIAMI, FL

DR. ALEJANDRO D. CHEDIAK
4300 ALTON RD., MIAMI, FL

DR. DAVID PERLMUTTER
720 GOODLETTE RD. N., STE. 203, NAPLES, FL

DR. MARTIN DAYTON
18600 COLLINS AVE., NORTH MIAMI BEACH, FL

DR. HARVEY J. GROSSBARD
17435 N.E. 12TH CT., NORTH MIAMI BEACH, FL

DR. GEORGE GRAVES
3501 N.E. 10TH ST., OCALA, FL

DR. GERALD BOUGHTON
640 N. VOLUSIA AVE., ORANGE CITY, FL

DR. TERESA M. BERNARD
1542 KINGSLEY AVE., STE. 132, ORANGE PARK, FL

DR. J. L. TOWNS
1820 PARK AVE., ORANGE PARK, FL

DR. MICHAEL DAPPALONIA
1043 TERRACE BLVD., ORLANDO, FL

DR. ROBERT S. THORNTON
601 E. ROLLINS ST., ORLANDO, FL

DR. PAUL LEVREAULT
1261 N. PINE HILLS RD., ORLANDO, FL

DR. MORRIS T. BIRD
601 E. ROLLINS ST., ORLANDO, FL

DR. HANA T. CHAIM
595 W. GRANADA BLVD., STE. D, ORMOND BEACH, FL

DR. NAIMA A. ELGHANY
710 VENETIAN WAY, PANAMA CITY, FL

DR. AHMED ELKADI
236 S. TYNDALL PKY., PANAMA CITY, FL

DR. HERBERT I. MOSELL
201 N.W. 82ND AVE., STE. 103, PLANTATION, FL

DR. KENNETH ARNOLD
1531 E. ATLANTIC BLVD., POMPANO BEACH, FL

DR. DEBRA A. GIBSON
1900 S. OCEAN BLVD., #9-G, POMPANO BEACH, FL

DR. J. E. WILLIAMS
238 N.E. 15TH TER., POMPANO BEACH, FL

DR. DAN C. ROEHN
3400 PK. CENTRAL BL. N., #3450, POMPANO BEACH, FL

DR. STEFANO DIMAURO
1333 S. STATE ROAD 7, POMPANO BEACH, FL

DR. MOKE W. WILLIAMS
50 N.E. 26TH AVE., STE. 302, POMPANO BEACH, FL

DR. R. J. McGEEHAN
11640 ZIMMERMAN RD., PORT RICHEY, FL

DR. GUY D. HOAGLAND
1004 BEVERLY DR., STE. B, ROCKLEDGE, FL

DR. ROBERT L. SCHAFER
P.O. BOX 262, RUSKIN, FL

DR. RAY C. WUNDERLICH
666 6TH ST. S., SAINT PETERSBURG, FL

DR. CARLOS F. BARBAS, JR.
8000 4TH ST. N., SAINT PETERSBURG, FL

DR. DAVID E. EATON
2891 53RD ST. N., SAINT PETERSBURG, FL

DR. NEIL T. FELDMAN
2525 PASADENA AVE. S., STE. S, SAINT PETERSBURG, FL

DR. GDUNCAN FINLAY
1700 S. TAMIAMI TRL., SARASOTA, FL

DR. SAMUEL SPECTOR
2030 BISPHAM RD., SARASOTA, FL

DR. STANLEY VAN PRAAG
5937 BENEVA RD., SARASOTA, FL

DR. HARVEY S. GARS
7168 SEMINOLE BLVD., SEMINOLE, FL

DR. MINA J. TAHERI-MILLER
206 ATLANTA AVE., STUART, FL

DR. DONALD J. CARROW
3902 HENDERSON BLVD., STE. 206, TAMPA, FL

DR. RALPH E. HELLAND
7202 E. BROADWAY AVE., TAMPA, FL

DR. M. J. WHITE
3715 W. AZEELE ST., TAMPA, FL

DR. DANIEL MADOCK
8005 N. 40TH ST., TAMPA, FL

DR. H. E. GILLIG
1278 MUIRFIELD CT., TITUSVILLE, FL

DR. DONALD WAGNER
1105 LAKEMONT DR., VALRICO, FL

DR. ALFRED S. MASSAM
528 W. MAIN ST., WAUCHULA, FL

DR. SALVADOR A. WILLIAMS
4825 BELVEDERE RD., WEST PALM BEACH, FL

DR. DOUGLAS PHILLIPS
4512 POINSETTIA AVE., WEST PALM BEACH, FL

DR. EDWARD ALTMAN
1490 S. MILITARY TRL., STE. 4, WEST PALM BEACH, FL

DR. JAMES W. MEDLOCK
2326 CONGRESS AVE. S., STE. 1-D, WEST PALM BEACH, FL

DR. JOSE E. SANCHEZ
2820 BUTLER BAY DR. N., WINDERMERE, FL

DR. ROBERT R. SMITH
1550 6TH ST. S.E., WINTER HAVEN, FL

DR. JAMES M. PARSONS
2699 LEE RD., STE, 303, WINTER PARK, FL

DR. JAMES C. MCKEE
2020 W. FAIRBANKS AVE., WINTER PARK, FL

DR. LINDSEY DE GUEHERY
267 W. COMSTOCK AVE., WINTER PARK, FL

DR. KENNETH W. HOOVER
5931 BRICK CT., STE. 100, WINTER PARK, FL

GEORGIA

DR. LASCA HOSPERS
4996 SUNSHINE CT., ACWORTH, GA

DR. D. M. BOYETTE
804 14TH AVE., ALBANY, GA

DR. JACK WOODARD
1304 WHISPERING PINES RD., ALBANY, GA

DR. FRANIS BUDA
300 BOULEVARD N.E., ATLANTA, GA

DR. MILTON FRIED
4426 TILLY MILL RD., ATLANTA, GA

DR. RUSSELL T. McDOUGAL
3312 PIEDMONT RD. N.E., STE. 345, ATLANTA, GA

DR. ROBERT A. SCHNAPPER
300 BOULEVARD N.E., ATLANTA, GA

DR. SIDI LEMNOUNI
41 PERIMETER PL. N.W., STE. 625, ATLANTA, GA

DR. STEPHEN EDELSON
3833 ROSWELL RD. N.E., STE. 110, ATLANTA, GA

DR. JOANNE WALTER
300 BOULEVARD N.E., ATLANTA, GA

DR. RUSSELL ROSENBERG
1000 JOHNSON FERRY RD. N.E., ATLANTA, GA

DR. DAVID EPSTEIN
427 MORELAND AVE. N.E., STE. 100, ATLANTA, GA

DR. WILLIAM E. RICHARDSON
1718 PEACHTREE ST. N.W., #522, ATLANTA, GA

DR. OLIVER L. GUNTER
24 N. ELLIS ST., CAMILLA, GA

DR. WILLARD GRAY
105 N. ERWIN ST., CARTERSVILLE, GA

DR. WILLIAM C. DOUGLAS
P.O. BOX 888, CLAYTON, GA

DR. STEPHEN B. EDELSON
5536 FLAT SHOALS PKY., DECATUR, GA

DR. ROBERT E. CONNELY
2698 LAWRENCEVILLE HWY., DECATUR, GA

DR. NANCI BISHOP
5908 FAIRBURN RD., DOUGLASVILLE, GA

DR. G. H. JOHNSON
227 INDUSTRIAL BLVD., DUBLIN, GA

DR. BERNARD MLAVER
4480 N. SHALLOWFORD RD., #222, DUNWOODY, GA

DR. CHARLES CROCKER
509 LEE ST., KINGSLAND, GA

DR. ALBERT NEHL
P.O. BOX 129, KINGSTON, GA

DR. RALPH LEE
110 LEWIS DR., STE. B, MARIETTA, GA

DR. JERRY HOCHMAN
1401 JOHNSON FERRY RD., MARIETTA, GA

DR. DIANE TALIK
1816 ASHBOROUGH RD., APT. C, MARIETTA, GA

DR. LAMAR FIELDS
P.O. BOX 1309, MILLEDGEVILLE, GA

DR. ALBERT NEHL
3700 HOLCOMB BRIDGE RD., NORCROSS, GA

DR. DAVID PAXTON
1011 N. 5TH AVE., ROME, GA

DR. JOEL A. GREENBERG
P.O. BOX 60129, SAVANNAH, GA

DR. TERRIL J. SCHNEIDER
205 DENTAL DR., STE 19, WARNER ROBINS, GA

HAWAII

DR. CAROL L. AMDUR
P.O. BOX 1232, HANALEI, HI

DR. JANET LINDSAY
1221 KAPIOLANI BLVD., #6A1, HONOLULU, HI

DR. STEVEN COOK
2919 KAPIOLANI BLVD., HONOLULU, HI

DR. DIANE OSTROFF
1750 KALAKAUA AVE., APT. 2107, HONOLULU, HI

DR. JACK L. BURKE
615 PIIKOI ST., PH. 3, HONOLULU HI

DR. LORI G. KIMATA
181 S. KUKUI ST., STE. 207, HONOLULU, HI

DR. PAUL KENYON
1314 S. KING ST., STE. 664, HONOLULU, HI

DR. HAZEL OGAWA-LERMAN
1150 S. KING ST., STE. 404, HONOLULU, HI

DR. JAMES W. PEARCE
888 S. KING ST., HONOLULU, HI

DR. GEORGE WEING
888 S. KING ST., HONOLULU, HI

DR. EDWARD J. MORGAN
347 N. KUAKINI ST., HONOLULU, HI

DR. V. G. CLARK-WISMER
1441 KAPIOLANI BLVD., #1113, HONOLULU, HI

DR. HERB J. BEY
2646 PAMOA RD., HONOLULU, HI

DR. MICHAEL L. TRAUB
75-5759 KUAKINI HWY., STE. 202, KAILUA KONA, HI

DR. KATHERINE D. POMEROY
P.O. BOX 2744, KAMUELA, HI

DR. WENDY RUNDEL
P.O. BOX 6714, KAMUELA, HI

DR. TATE ROLFS
47-730 HUI KELU ST., APT. 1, KANEOHE, HI

DR. FRED GEORGE
6016 KAWAIHAU RD., KAPAA, HI

DR. ROBERT ZELKOVSKY
5356 KUMOLE ST., KAPAA, HI

DR. SCOTT BASTO
P.O. BOX 1237, KAPAA, HI

DR. ARRINGTON
P.O. BOX 649, KEALAKEKUA, HI

DR. CLIFTON ARRINGTON
P.O. BOX 649, KEALAKEKUA, HI

DR. LILLIAN CUNNINGHAM
113A KULALANI DR., KULA, HI

DR. MICHAEL J. DICKENS
P.O. BOX 307, LAHAINA, HI

DR. JONATHAN C. MATHER
P.O. BOX 477, LAUPAHOEHOE, HI

DR. CATHERINE M. DOWNEY
3093 AKAHI ST., LIHUE, HI

DR. STEVEN G. DUBEY
3093 AKAHI ST., LIIIUE, HI

DR. MILES GREENBERG
P.O. BOX 3188, LIHUE, HI

DR. JEFF BAKER
P.O. BOX 217, MAKAWAO, HI

DR. KEVIN DAVISON
2119B W. VINEYARD ST., WAILUKU, HI

IDAHO

DR. H. G. VODICKA
2975 OVERLAND AVE., BURLEY, ID

DR. MICKY HALL
13440 E. MARIE CREEK RD., COEUR DE ALENE, ID

DR. CHARLES T. MCGEE
1717 LINCOLN WAY, STE. 108, COEUR D ALENE, ID

DR. STEPHEN THORNBURGH
824 17TH AVE. S., NAMPA, ID

DR. MILTON NELSON
447 N. 1800 E., SAINT ANTHONY, ID

DR. SAMUEL WAGNER
502 N. 4TH AVE., SANDPOINT, ID

DR. TIM BIRDSALL
7005 E. SELLE RD., SANDPOINT, ID

ILLINOIS

DR. STEVEN G. AYRE
915 TOFT AVE., ANTIOCH, IL

DR. WILLIAM J. MAUER
3401 N. KENNICOTT AVE., ARLINGTON HEIGHTS, IL

DR. ALLEN AVEN
1120 E. CENTRAL RD., ARLINGTON HEIGHTS, IL

DR. TERRILL K. HAWS
121 S. WILKE RD., STE. 111, ARLINGTON HEIGHTS, IT

DR. W. J. KESSLER
105 S. 5TH ST., AUBURN, IL

DR. MARITE GROTHMAN
845 N. LAKE ST., AURORA, IL

DR. THOMAS HESSELINK
888 S. EDGELAWN DR., STE. 1735, AURORA, IL

DR. THERON RANDOLPH
700 W. FABYAN PKY., BATAVIA, IL

DR. T. HESSELINK
554 S. MAIN ST., BELVIDERE, IL

DR. PHILIP J. BERENT
125 E. LAKE COOK RD., BUFFALO GROVE, IL

DR. RONALD F. POKORNOWSKI
381 S. MAIN PL., CAROL STREAM, IL

DR. HUGH A. JENKINS
2148 W. 95TH ST., CHICAGO, IL

DR. GLORIA BOWMAN
4950 W. IRVING PARK RD., CHICAGO, IL

DR. GREGORY KAUFMAN
3029 N. PULASKI RD., CHICAGO, IL

DR. ALEXANNE OSINSKI
4832 N. KENMORE AVE., #3, CHICAGO, IL

DR. JEAN-PAUL SPIRE
5841 S. MARYLAND AVE., CHICAGO, IL

DR. MARK A. SZYMANSKI
3654 N. NEVA AVE., CHICAGO, IL

DR. EDWARD KOZIOL
5439 N. MAGNET AVE., CHICAGO, IL

DR. ANDREW PASMINSKI
1342 W. BELMONT AVE., CHICAGO, IL

DR. SHELIA LEIDY
2400 N. ASHLAND AVE., CHICAGO, IL

DR. LATA BHAVNANI
2400 N. ASHLAND AVE., CHICAGO, IL

DR. ZHENGANG GUO
327A E. 23RD ST., CHICAGO, IL

DR. ULF HENRICSSON
2400 N. ASHLAND AVE., CHICAGO, IL

DR. ARCHANA LAL
2400 N. ASHLAND AVE., CHICAGO, IL

DR. RECECCA QI
2400 N. ASHLAND AVE., CHICAGO, IL

DR. CANDACE NOWAK
2400 N. ASHLAND AVE., CHICAGO, IL

DR. TIMOTHY W. FIOR
7249 N. WESTERN AVE., CHICAGO, IL

DR. PATRICK V. NUZZO
2400 N. ASHLAND AVE., CHICAGO, IL

DR. DAN PLOVANICH
2400 N. ASHLAND AVE., CHICAGO, IL

DR. DANIEL SHAIN
2400 N. ASHLAND AVE., CHICAGO, IL

DR. ROSALIND CARTWRIGHT
1653 W. CONGRESS PKY., CHICAGO, IL

DR. MARK H. LABEAU
46 E. OAK ST., STE. 200, CHICAGO, IL

DR. GORDON SIEGEL
55 E. WASHINGTON ST., STE. 2705, CHICAGO, IL

DR. LEANNE APFELBECK
1422 N. HOYNE AVE., #3, CHICAGO, IL

DR. ANATOLY SUBOTA
3848 W. IRVING PARK RD., CHICAGO, IL

DR. JAMES CORZINE
210 W. MARKET ST., CHRISTOPHER, IL

DR. GARY R. OBERG
31 N. VIRGINIA ST., CRYSTAL LAKE, IL

DR. W. R. ELGHAMMER
723 N. LOGAN AVE., DANVILLE, IL

DR. LAURENCE S. WEBSTER
3090 N. MAIN ST., DECATUR, IL

DR. MICHAEL J. ZIA
2300 N. EDWARD ST., DECATUR, IL

DR. DIANE MURAD
1155 DEERFIELD RD. #1A, DEERFIELD, IL

DR. RONALD WILLIAMS
325 S. MAIN ST., DEPEW, IL

DR. LAURA AMES
1104 W. JEFFERSON AVE., EFFINGHAM, IL

DR. JOHN J. DAWSON
706 W. MAIN ST., ELMWOOD, IL

DR. THEODORE TEPAS
1012 LAKE SHORE BLVD., EVANSTON, IL

DR. RICHARD S. ROSENBERG
2650 RIDGE AVE., EVANSTON, IL

DR. MING-TE LIN
3235 VOLLMER RD., STE. 142, FLOSSMOOR, IL

DR. RICHARD E. HRDLICKA
302 RANDALL RD., #206, GENEVA, IL

DR. PETER G. GILBERT
P.O. BOX 447, GENEVA, IL

DR. ROBERT S. WATERS
739 ROOSEVELT RD., GLEN ELLYN, IL

DR. JUDITH RENINGER
159 NORTH AVE., #330, GLENDALE HEIGHTS, IL

DR. TOM O'BRYAN
1500 WAUKEGAN RD., STE. 200, GLENVIEW, IL

DR. ARNOLD HOUSER
18403 S. HALSTED ST., GLENWOOD, IL

DR. WALT STOLL
267 YORKSHIRE CT., GURNEE, IL

DR. SAMUEL PERVA
210 SKOKIE VALLEY RD., HIGHLAND PARK, IL

DR. OELE PALY
P.O. BOX 1115, HINES, IL

DR. GEORGE E. SHAMBAUGH, JR.
40 S. CLAY ST., HINSDALE, IL

DR. GUERDON BAKER
35756 N. HUNT AVE., INGLESIDE, IL

DR. KATHLEEN LINDSEY
P.O. BOX 122, ISLAND LAKE, IL

DR. BRIAN CECIL
5302 S. CATHERINE AVE., LA GRANGE, IL

DR. PATRICIA MENNER
165 S. RAND RD., LAKE ZURICH, IL

DR. STEPHEN HAUGEN
2S115 LLOYD AVE., LOMBARD, IL

DR. ANICETO M. D'SOUSA
1110H N. GREEN ST., McHENRY, IL

DR. CARL BYER
1733 W. ALGONQUIN RD., MOUNT PROSPECT, IL

DR. THERON G. RANDOLPH
161 S. LINCOLNWAY ST., STE. 305, N. AURORA, IL

DR. PAUL J. DUNN
715 LAKE ST., OAK PARK, IL

DR. JERRY E. HUTCHISON
6901 NORTH AVE., OAK PARK, IL

DR. FRANK YUROSEK
816 S. OAK PARK AVE., OAK PARK, IL

DR. THOMAS E. BENSON
1200 N. EAST ST., OLNEY, IL

DR. DAVID LEGER
263 N. MERCHANTS DR., OSWEGO, IL

DR. TERRY W. LOVE
645 W. MAIN ST., OTTAWA, IL

DR. HERBERT WEINSTEIN
2627 N. KNOXVILLE AVE., PEORIA, IL

DR. RONALD J. LYSS
3105 18TH AVE., ROCK ISLAND, IL

DR. GERALD F. STAUB
1400 CHARLES ST., ROCKFORD, IL

DR. THOMAS L. STONE
1811 HICKS RD., ROLLING MEADOWS, IL

DR. THOMAS DRZEMALA
360 E. IRVING PARK RD., ROSELLE, IL

DR. JEANNE M. QUAID
15821 S. PARK AVE., SOUTH HOLLAND, IL

DR. JOSEPH KARINATTU
100 E. 5TH ST., TILTON, IL

DR. DANIEL R. DIESKA
17726 OAK PARK AVE., STE. A, TINLEY PARK, IL

DR. DONALD A. GREELEY
602 W. UNIVERSITY AVE., URBANA, IL

DR. DANIEL PICCHIETTI
602 W. UNIVERSITY AVE., URBANA, IL

DR. MOHAMMAD T. GHANI
10301 W. ROOSEVELT RD., WESTCHESTER, IL

DR. RUTH C. MARTENS
1913 GLADSTONE DR., WHEATON, IL

DR. PAULINE HARDING
27W281 GENEVA RD., STE. D, WINFIELD, IL

DR. NORENE B. HESS
700 OAK ST., WINNETKA, IL

DR. ROBERT T. MARSHALL
700 OAK ST., WINNETKA, IL

DR. ALVIN GRAUN
7350 JANES AVE., WOODRIDGE, IL

DR. PETER SENATORE
1911 27TH ST., ZION, IL

INDIANA

DR. GAWRY YOUNG
3728 MAIN ST., ANDERSON, IN

DR. THOMAS STEVENS
1440 N. 200 W., #C, ANGOLA, IN

DR. LUCINDA JORDAN
702 W. 5TH ST, BLOOMINGTON, IN

DR. JOHN L. ZETTELMAIER
374 INDIAN BOUNDARY RD., CHESTERTON, IN

DR. MARK A. SCHNEIDER
145 S. NAPPANEE ST., ELKHART, IN

DR. JEROME WINIGER
721 N. MAIN ST., EVANSVILLE, IN

DR. HAROLD T. SPARKS
3001 WASHINGTON AVE., EVANSVILLE, IN

DR. JOY L. MARTIN
600 E. WALNUT ST., #11, EVANSVILLE, IN

DR. JOHN F. O'BRIAN
3217 LAKE AVE., FORT WAYNE, IN

DR. ALAN W. SIDEL
5110 N. CLINTON ST., FORT WAYNE, IN

DR. CAL STRECTER
9635 SARIC CT., HIGHLAND, IN

DR. KENNETH WIESERT
3232 N. MERIDIAN ST., INDIANAPOLIS, IN

DR. EVELYN EARLEY
652 E. 54TH ST., INDIANAPOLIS, IN

DR. DAVID DARBRO
2124 E. HANNA AVE., INDIANAPOLIS, IN

DR. MARVIN E. VOLLMER
1500 N. RITTER AVE., INDIANAPOLIS, IN

DR. ROBERT ARMER
8803 N. MERIDIAN ST., INDIANAPOLIS, IN

DR. PREMALA E. BREWSTER
8170 RAVEN ROCK DR., INDIANAPOLIS, IN

DR. EUGENE TROUT
502 E. CULVER RD., KNOX, IN

DR. FREDERICK ROBINSON
2400 SOUTH ST., LAFAYETTE, IN

DR. ROBERT R. CANIDA
904 E. 1ST ST., MADISON, IN

DR. THOMAS GOODWIN
6111 HARRISON ST., #343, MERRILLVILLE, IN

DR. ROBERT THOMAS
422 FRANKLIN ST., MICHIGAN CITY, IN

DR. NORMAN E. WHITNEY
P.O. BOX 173, MOORESVILLE, IN

DR. JOHN C. PETERSON
2423 W. JACKSON ST., MUNCIE, IN

DR. EDWARD S. KAWECKI
8235 CALUMET AVE., #B, MUNSTER, IN

DR. ALAN B. McDANIEL
1919 STATE ST., STE. 100, NEW ALBANY, IN

DR. LAURENCE S. WEBSTER
547 LIONS CREEK DR., NOBLESVILLE, IN

DR. JANE HOBING
1616 SCOTTSWOOD DR., SOUTH BEND, IN

DR. DAVID E. TURFLER
336 W. NAVARRE ST., SOUTH BEND, IN

DR. WILLIAM EDWARDS
1044 MAIN ST., TELL CITY, IN

DR. HENRY J. MATICK
520 S. 7TH ST., VINCENNES, IN

IOWA

DR. STANLEY FITZGERALD
416 S.W. 3RD ST., ANKENY, IA

DR. JAROSLAVA ODVARKO
1618 GRANT ST., BETTENDORF, IA

DR. VERN L. HAGEN
3012 PARKWILD DR., BETTENDORF, IA

DR. MICHAEL H. LAWS
1401 W. CENTRAL PARK AVE., DAVENPORT, IA

DR. JOHN VAN CLEAVE
8345 UNIVERSITY BLVD., DES MOINES, IA

DR. NORRIS BOWLER
8564 ALICE AVE., DES MOINES, IA

DR. ROBERT W. SOLL
1044 4TH ST., DES MOINES, IA

DR. DANIEL J. DIXON
P.O. BOX 442, FAIRFIELD, IA

DR. PHILIP LANSKY
221 E MARKET ST., #304, IOWA CITY, IA

DR. NYLE D. KAUFFMAN
2460 TOWNCREST DR., IOWA CITY, IA

DR. L. A. STEFFENSMEIER
122 E. MAIN ST., LISBON, IA

DR. GLORIA HARRINGTON
1022 COURT AVE., MARENGO, IA

DR. MARTIN G. MEINDL
1190 BRIARSTONE DR., MASON CITY, IA

DR. RICHARD BOYER
701 PARK AVE., MUSCATINE, IA

DR. HORST G. BLUME
700 JENNINGS ST., SIOUX CITY, IA

DR. V. T. RILEY
501 SYCAMORE ST., WATERLOO, IA

KANSAS

DR. MAX L. LONG
417 N.W. 3RD ST., ABILENE, KS

DR. STEVENS B. ACKER
P.O. BOX 483, ANDOVER, KS

DR. TIM WEILERT
802 S. HIGHLAND ST., CHANUTE, KS

DR. JAMES L. PARMELE
305 N. MINNESOTA AVE., COLUMBUS, KS

DR. TERRY HUNSBERGER
602 N. 3RD ST., GARDEN CITY, KS

DR. MARION CALLAHAN
216 E. PARK ST., GARDNER, KS

DR. CHARLES L. JULIAN
1510 W. LAUREL ST., INDEPENDENCE, KS

DR. JOHN GAMBLE, JR.
1509 QUINDARO BLVD., KANSAS CITY, KS

DR. ARTHUR P. DOWELL
501 N. MUR LEN RD., OLATHE, KS

DR. GAYLE COOK
617 S. 6TH ST., OSAGE CITY, KS

DR. JOHN M. BROCKWAY
1408 S. MAIN ST., OTTAWA, KS

DR. STEPHANIE RASMUSSEN
1900 W. 75TH ST., STE. 210, PRAIRIE VILLAGE, KS

DR. KIMBERLY SHARA
6220 ANTIOCH RD., SHAWNEE MISSION, KS

DR. GRACE BREWER
7199 W. 98TH TER., STE. 150, SHAWNEE MISSION, KS

DR. CHARLES LAVALLEY
2120 S.W. BRANDYWINE LN., TOPEKA, KS

DR. TED W. DAUGHETY
1700 S.W. 7TH ST., TOPEKA, KS

DR. DARYL POKEA
RR 8 BOX 45, TOPEKA, KS

DR. CHARLES HINSHAW
1833 N. ROCK ROAD CT., WICHITA, KS

DR. STANLEY BEYERLE
2708 E. CENTRAL AVE., WICHITA, KS

DR. HUGH D. RIORDAN
3100 N. HILLSIDE ST., WICHITA, KS

KENTUCKY

DR. JOHN C. TAPP
414 OLD MORGANTOWN RD., BOWLING GREEN, KY

DR. ROSANNE CUNNINGHAM
250 PARK ST., BOWLING GREEN, KY

DR. STEPHEN W. JENNINGS
85 N. GRAND AVE., FORT THOMAS, KY

DR. DAVID MYNTHER
85 N. GRAND AVE., FORT THOMAS, KY

DR. M. N. MARTIN
206 LEXINGTON ST., LANCASTER, KY

DR. JOHN H. PARKS
436 E. 2ND ST., LEXINGTON, KY

DR. ROBERT GRANACHER, JR.
1 SAINT JOSEPH DR., LEXINGTON, KY

DR. DAVID WINSLOW
1 AUDUBON PLAZA DR., LOUISVILLE, KY

DR. BARBARA J. RIGDON
530 S. JACKSON ST., LOUISVILLE, KY

DR. NANINE HENDERSON
4010 DUPONT CIR., STE. 200, LOUISVILLE, KY

DR. ROBERT W. LAVELY
7300 LA GRANGE RD., LOUISVILLE, KY

DR. BARBARA KUNKLE
920 S. MAIN ST., MADISONVILLE, KY

DR. J. H. ENSOR
123 E. 3RD ST., MAYSVILLE, KY

DR. WALT STOLL
6801 DANVILLE RD., NICHOLASVILLE, KY

DR. STEPHEN S. KITECK
1301 PUMPHOUSE RD., SOMERSET, KY

LOUISIANA

DR. STEPHANIE F. CAVE
7777 HENNESSY BLVD., STE. 101, BATON ROUGE, LA

DR. JEWELL WARREN
7171 AIRLINE HWY., STE. 1, BATON ROUGE, LA

DR. SUNNY COOPER
255 BEVERLY DR., BATON ROUGE, LA

DR. SAROJ T. TAMPIRA
812 E. JUDGE PEREZ DR., CHALMETTE, LA

DR. SARAH J. COLE
2750 RICHLAND ST., KENNER, LA

DR. ERWIN BIXENMAN
107 S. COLLEGE RD., LAFAYETTE, LA

DR. THOMAS J. CALLENDER
108 HAROLYN PARK DR., LAFAYETTE, LA

DR. RAYMOND LEBLEU
4008 ERNEST ST., LAKE CHARLES, LA

DR. JAMES A. ANDREWS
639 W. CAUSEWAY APPROACH, MANDEVILLE, LA

DR. ROY M. MONTALBANO
4408 HIGHWAY 22, MANDEVILLE, LA

DR. EDNA DOYLE
4224 HOUMA BLVD., STE. 470, METAIRIE, LA

DR. PHILLIP MITCHELL
407 BIENVILLE ST., NATCHITOCHES, LA

DR. ADONIS J. DOMINGUE
602 N. LEWIS ST., #600, NEW IBERIA, LA

DR. ELIZABETH BOULDIN
1415 TULANE AVE., NEW ORLEANS, LA

DR. JAMES P. CARTER
1430 TULANE AVE., NEW ORLEANS, LA

DR. JOSEPH R. WHITAKER
P.O. BOX 458, NEWELLTON, LA

DR. SIDNEY DUPOIS
P.O. BOX 125, SAINT MARTINVILLE, LA

DR. FELIX K. PRAKASAM
P.O. BOX 3153, SHREVEPORT, LA

DR. ANDREW L. CHESSON JR
P.O. BOX 33932, SHREVEPORT, LA

MAINE

DR. MARY LYNN GARNER
4 MILK ST., PORTLAND, ME

MARYLAND

DR. JACOB E. TEITERBAUMM
139 OLD SOLOMONS ISLAND RD., ANNAPOLIS, MD

DR. WILLIAM BORO
49 OLD SOLOMONS ISLAND RD., ANNAPOLIS, MD

DR. THOMAS E. HOBBINS
8415 BELLONA LN., STE. 211, BALTIMORE, MD

DR. RICHARD E. LAYTON
901 DULANEY VALLEY RD. #602, BALTIMORE, MD

DR. PAUL R. COOK
901 DULANEY VALLEY RD., BALTIMORE, MD

DR. NEIL SOLOMON
901 DULANEY VALLEY RD., BALTIMORE, MD

DR. NEAL BLAXBERG
10 CHURCH LN., BALTIMORE, MD

DR. BARBARA SOLOMON
8109 HARFORD RD., BALTIMORE, MD

DR. TIMOTHY CITRO
5201 EAST DR., BALTIMORE, MD

DR. BENJAMIN ROTHSTEIN
2835 SMITH AVE., STE. 209, BALTIMORE, MD

DR. PETER HINDERBERGER
4801 YELLOWWOOD AVE., BALTIMORE, MD

DR. ROBERT POANE
5 BEL AIR SOUTH PKY., #L1215, BEL AIR, MD

DR. G. D. BEECH
9213 SEVEN LOCKS RD., BETHESDA, MD

DR. HENRY MILLS
6911 LAUREL BOWIE RD. #206, BOWIE, MD

DR. WYRTH P. BAKER
4701 WILLARD AVE., CHEVY CHASE, MD

DR. DENISE CONNER
4321 HARTWICK RD., STE. 406, COLLEGE PARK, MD

DR. THOMAS LO
1438 DEFENSE HWY., GAMBRILLS, MD

DR. PREMALA E. BREWSTER
7606 23RD AVE., HYATTSVILLE, MD

DR. PAUL V. BEALS
9101 CHERRY LN., APT. 205, LAUREL, MD

DR. DANIEL T. WISE
14307 JARRETTSVILLE PIKE, PHOENIX, MD

DR. ALAN R. GABY
31 WALKER AVE., PIKESVILLE, MD

DR. DAVID G. WEMBER
26 GUY CT., ROCKVILLE, MD

DR. KONRAD W. BAKKER
9715 MEDICAL CENTER DR., ROCKVILLE, MD

DR. ANTHONY M. AURIGEMMA
1401 SPRING ST., STE. 200, SILVER SPRING, MD

DR. MONIQUE MANIET
7330 CARROLL AVE., TAKOMA PARK, MD

MASSACHUSETTS

DR. BETTY WOOD
24 MINOT AVE., ACTON, MA

DR. VIRGINIA HARPER
190 UNIVERSITY DR., AMHERST, MA

DR. AMY B. ROTHENBERG
356 MIDDLE ST., AMHERST, MA

DR. SAMUEL GLADSTONE
12 DICKINSON ST., AMHERST, MA

DR. MICHAEL JANSON
P.O. BOX 732, BARNSTABLE, MA

DR. LARRY L. RAFFEL
101 DOUGLAS RD., BELMONT, MA

DR. JANET L. LEVATIN
1993 DORCHESTER AVE., BOSTON, MA

DR. NICOLAS P. CARBALLEIRA
95 BERKELEY ST., BOSTON, MA

DR. J. W. WEISS
330 BROOKLINE AVE., #KS430, BOSTON, MA

DR. GUILLERMO R. ASIS
167 COREY RD., #100, BROOKLINE, MA

DR. MICHAEL JANSON
2557 MASSACHUSETTS AVE., CAMBRIDGE, MA

DR. STEELE BELOK
33 GARDEN ST., CAMBRIDGE, MA

DR. EDWARD R. ELLIS, JR.
6 COURTHOUSE LN., STE. 9, CHELMSFORD, MA

DR. LAUREN FOX-O'NEAL
15 WYOMING AVE., FALMOUTH, MA

DR. SIDNEY SKINNER
103 COUNTRY CLUB RD., GREENFIELD, MA

DR. RICHARD COHEN
51 MILL ST., STE. 1, HANOVER, MA

DR. JAMES M. LEMKIN
7 COLE RD., HAYDENVILLE, MA

DR. R. G. MALLADI
1221 MAIN ST., HOLYOKE, MA

DR. CHRISTINE LUTHRA
54 ROCKVIEW ST., JAMAICA PLAIN, MA

DR. JANET K. BEATY
5 SMITH AVE., LEXINGTON, MA

DR. SVETLANA KAUFMAN
24 MERRIMACK ST., STE. 323, LOWELL, MA

DR. LEONARD M. HOROWITZ
119 ROCKAWAY AVE., MARBLEHEAD, MA

DR. PHILIP LANSKY
75 NORTH ST., MATTAPOISETT, MA

DR. MARIE A. MANSON-WEBB
53 OLD ROWLEY RD., NEWBURY, MA

DR. DANIEL A. KINDERLEHRER
65 NEWBURYPORT TPKE., NEWBURY, MA

DR. JAMES P. DOYLE
555 COMMONWEALTH AVE., NEWTON, MA

DR. JEANNE T. HUBBUCH
1340 CENTRE ST., STE. 203, NEWTON, MA

DR. LISA A. HARVEY
16 CENTER ST., STE. 523, NORTHAMPTON, MA

DR. J. A. HERSCHFUS
P.O. BOX 336, SHARON, MA

DR. ROBERT G. SIDORSKY
RR 2, SHELBURNE FALLS, MA

ACCUPUNCTURE & MEDICAL ARTS CENTER
15 KENWOOD ST., SOMERVILLE, MA

DR. DEEPAK CHOPRA
P.O. BOX 598, SOUTH LANCASTER, MA

DR. SHELDON S. GOLDBERG
2 MEDICAL CENTER DR., STE. 110, SPRINGFIELD, MA

DR. RICHARD MOSKOWITZ
173 MOUNT AUBURN ST., WATERTOWN, MA

DR. JOSEPH P. KEENAN
75 SPRINGFIELD RD., WESTFIELD, MA

DR. JEFFREY LEVY
71 ASHFIELD RD., WILLIAMSBURG, MA

DR. ROSS S. McCONNELL
732 MAIN ST., WILLIAMSTOWN, MA

MICHIGAN

DR. ROBERT TRIPODI
315 W. HURON ST., #320A, ANN ARBOR, MI

DR. DENNIS K. CHERNIN
2345 S. HURON PKY., ANN ARBOR, MI

DR. MARSHA L. TRAXLER
544 3RD ST., ANN ARBOR, MI

DR. WILLIAM T. ALLEN
P.O. BOX 995, ANN ARBOR, MI

DR. REZO HOWZE
5577 PLYMOUTH RD., ANN ARBOR, MI

DR. EDWARD J. LINKNER
2345 S. HURON PKY., ANN ARBOR, MI

DR. PAULA DAVEY
425 E. WASHINGTON ST., STE. 201, ANN ARBOR, MI

DR. EDWARD LINKER
2345 S. HURON PKY., ANN ARBOR, MI

DR. ROBERT D. ROUSSEAU
6405 TELEGRAPH RD., #J-3, BLOOMFIELD HILLS, MI

DR. MARGARET PARIS
8018 GRANADA AVE., BRIGHTON, MI

DR. H. W. WINSTANLEY
625 W. 14 MILE RD., CLAWSON, MI

DR. JERRY A. WALKER
5681 N. BEECH DALY RD., DEARBORN HEIGHTS, MI

DR. FRANK ZORICK
2799 W. GRAND BLVD., DETROIT, MI

DR. FARRIS L. LOVELL
19207 SCHAEFER HWY., DETROIT, MI

DR. HARLEY J. ROBINSON
20101 GREENFIELD RD., DETROIT, MI

DR. ALBERT J. SCARCHILLI
30275 W. 13 MILE RD., FARMINGTON, MI

DR. WILLIAM M. BERNARD
1044 GILBERT RD., FLINT, MI

DR. KENNETH GANAPINI
1044 GILBERT RD., FLINT, MI

DR. GERALD KEYTE
388 INKSTER RD., INKSTER, MI

DR. NANCY EOS
P.O. BOX 417, LAKELAND, MI

DR. LYNNE M. FRIDAY
5346 MAIN ST., LEXINGTON, MI

DR. MARVIN D. PENWELL
319 N. BRIDGE ST., LINDEN, MI

DR. HERBERT L. CAMP
4011 ORCHARD DR., STE. 3004, MIDLAND, MI

DR. GEORGE DUBBS
122 NEW ST., MOUNT CLEMENS, MI

DR. DAVID W. REGIANI
101 SOUTH ST., STE. 458, ORTONVILLE, MI

DR. VAHAGN AGBABIAN
28 N. SAGINAW ST., STE. 1105, PONTIAC, MI

DR. RICHARD E. TAPERT
23550 HARPER AVE., SAINT CLAIR SHORE, MI

DR. STEPHEN D. NUGENT
25755 SOUTHFIELD RD., STE. N20, SOUTHFIELD, MI

DR. HARRY R. BUTLER
1821 KING RD., TRENTON, MI

DR. CORNELIUS DERRICK
1821 KING RD., TRENTON, MI

DR. NORMAN A. WIMPSON
2171 W. JEFFERSON AVE., #305, TRENTON, MI

DR. RAHU B. SANGAL
44199 DEQUINDRE RD., #311, TROY, MI

DR. GREGORY KRUSZEWSKI
4101 JOHN R RD., STE. 100, TROY, MI

DR. DENNIS G. CHARNESKY
4101 JOHN R RD., STE. 100, TROY, MI

DR. GERALD D. KEYTE
58024 VAN DYKE RD., WASHINGTON, MI

DR. JEFFREY TULIN-SILVER
6330 ORCHARD LAKE RD., #110, W. BLOOMFIELD, MI

DR. ROBERT A. BREAKEY
4972 W. CLARK RD., STE. 101, YPSILANTI, MI

MINNESOTA

DR. G. W. JONES
19644 CLEARY RD. N.W., ANOKA, MN

DR. KAREN B. BALTZELL
555 EDGEWOOD DR. N., BRAINERD, MN

DR. HARLEN D. WHITLING
927 TRETTEL LN., CLOQUET, MN

DR. PETER K. FRANKLIN
407 E. 3RD ST., DULUTH, MN

DR. VIRGINIA SHAPIRO
2111 E. SUPERIOR ST., DULUTH, MN

DR. KRISTIN A. BROWN
5101 VERNON AVE. S., STE. 502, EDINA, MN

DR. WILLIAM BRAUER
2545 CHICAGO AVE., MINNEAPOLIS, MN

DR. A. B. BORAAS
2830 CEDAR AVE. S., MINNEAPOLIS, MN

DR. STEVEN E. KLOS
2421 W. 42ND ST., MINNEAPOLIS, MN

DR. MARK MAHOWALD
701 PARK AVE., MINNEAPOLIS, MN

DR. JANE M. JESS
1250 HENNEPIN AVE., MINNEAPOLIS, MN

DR. KEITH SEHNERT
6250 EXCELSIOR BLVD., MINNEAPOLIS, MN

DR. ANDREW J. LUCKING
3546 GRAND AVE., MINNEAPOLIS, MN

DR. RACHAEL TROCKMAN
701 PARK AVE., MINNEAPOLIS, MN

DR. WALTER L. WILDER
6525 DREW AVE. S., MINNEAPOLIS, MN

DR. JOHN L. WILSON, JR.
224 7TH ST. N., MORA, MN

DR. PAUL W. SWAN
P.O. BOX 389, PELICAN RAPIDS, MN

DR. JOHN W. SHEPARD
200 1ST ST. S.W., ROCHESTER, MN

DR. TED BERMAN
6500 EXCELSIOR BLVD., SAINT LOUIS PARK, MN

DR. HELEN C. HEALY
1365 ENGLEWOOD AVE., STE. 102, SAINT PAUL, MN

DR. JOSEPH DONOHOE
821 RAYMOND AVE. STE. 240, SAINT PAUL, MN

DR. MARY E. RUTHERFORD
555 7TH ST. W., SAINT PAUL, MN

DR. RUSSELL DES MARAIS
569 SELBY AVE,, SAINT PAUL, MN

DR. THOMAS F. MULROONEY
69 EXCHANGE ST, W., SAINT PAUL, MN

DR. KEITH CARLSON
P.O. BOX 718, TYLER, MN

DR. SHARON D. GOOSMANN
200 4TH ST. S.W., STE. 22, WILLMAR, MN

MISSISSIPPI

DR. SYDNEY SMITH
P.O. BOX 1810, GULFPORT, MS

DR. GEORFREY B. HARTWIG
P.O. BOX 16389, HATTIESBURG, MS

DR. ANWANTBIR CHAWLA
2500 N. STATE ST., JACKSON, MS

DR. ROLAND K. HARRIS
975 W. RIDGE DR., JACKSON, MS

DR. ROBERT T. CATES
410 SAINT AUGUSTINE DR., MADISON, MS

DR. JAMES H. WADDELL
1520 GOVERNMENT ST., OCEAN SPRINGS, MS

DR. THOMAS GLASGON
2161 S. LAMAR BLVD., OXFORD, MS

DR. ROBERT HOLLINGSWORTH
P.O. BOX 87, SHELBY, MS

MISSOURI

DR. ROBERT HAISLUP
667 WALNUT POINT CT., BALLWIN, MO

DR. FRANK STARK
713 CHERRY ST., CHILLICOTHE, MO

DR. BEVERLY MILES
1301 TORREY PINES DR., COLUMBIA, MO

DR. JOHN T. SCHWENT
1400 N. TRUMAN BLVD., FESTUS, MO

DR. GARRY VICKAR
1245 GRAHAM RD., FLORISSANT, MO

DR. TIPU SULTAN
4585 WASHINGTON ST., FLORISSANT, MO

DR. TOM SMITH
3935 PARKER RD., FLORISSANT, MO

DR. ALBERT NEHL
151 FLOWER VALLEY SHOP CTR., FLORISSANT, MO

DR. BRUCE A. STAYTON
1212 W. TRUMAN RD., INDEPENDENCE, MO

DR. JAMES E. SWANN
2116 S. STERLING AVE., INDEPENDENCE, MO

DR. LAWRENCE E. DORMAN
9120 E. 35TH ST. S., INDEPENDENCE, MO

DR. RALPH D. COOPER
1608 E. 20TH ST., JOPLIN, MO

DR. NED HEESE
2646 N.W. PLATTE RD., KANSAS CITY, MO

DR. N. C. FRENCH
3335 E. 113TH TER., #B, KANSAS CITY, MO

DR. EDWARD W. MCDONAGH
2800 KENDALLWOOD PKY., STE. A, KANSAS CITY, MO

DR. JAMES L. ROWLAND
8133 WORNALL RD., KANSAS CITY, MO

DR. SHARI AKERY
7445 WYOMING ST., KANSAS CITY, MO

DR. ANN ROMAKER
4400 WORNALL RD., KANSAS CITY, MO

DR. NORMAN RICKY
10515 BLUE RIDGE BLVD., #207, KANSAS CITY, MO

DR. JON D. MAGEE
2316 E. MEYER BLVD., KANSAS CITY, MO

DR. DOYLE B. HILL
601 N. BUSCH AVE., MOUNTAIN GROVE, MO

DR. WILLIAM L. TRAXEL
666 LESTER ST., POPLAR BLUFF, MO

DR. EMERSON W. IRELAND
703 WOLLARD BLVD., RICHMOND, MO

DR. SYLVIA BARTLETT
HC 35 BOX 430, ROLLA, MO

DR. MARTIN H. CHRIST
1402 FARAON ST., SAINT JOSEPH, MO

DR. GERALD N. BART
12700 SOUTHFORK RD., STE. 200, SAINT LOUIS, MO

DR. DAVID ROZEBOOM
8428 DELMAR BLVD., SAINT LOUIS, MO

DR. KRISTYNA M. HARTSE
1221 S. GRAND BLVD., SAINT LOUIS, MO

DR. JOSEPH UNGER, JR.
4224 WATSON RD., SAINT LOUIS, MO

DR. J. H. WALKER
138 N. MERAMEC AVE., SAINT LOUIS, MO

DR. KENNETH L. MOSS
6150 OAKLAND AVE., SAINT LOUIS, MO

DR. JAMES KINNARD
605 S. 1ST ST., SAVANNAH, MO

SHEALY INSTITUTE
1328 E. EVERGREEN ST., SPRINGFIELD, MO

DR. EDWARD GWIN
3800 S. NATIONAL AVE., STE. LI, SPRINGFIELD, MO

DR. JOHN T. HADDER
1320 S. GLENSTONE AVE., #12A, SPRINGFIELD, MO

DR. C. N. SHEALY
1328 E. EVERGREEN ST., SPRINGFIELD, MO

DR. WILLIAM C. SUNDERWIRTH
2828 N. NATIONAL AVE., SPRINGFIELD, MO

DR. W. C. SUNERWIRTH
307 EAST ST., STOCKTON, MO

DR. RONALD H. SCOTT
750 PASCAL ST., SULLIVAN, MO

DR. HAYES CLINTON
100 W. MAIN ST., UNION, MO

DR. SUSAN STOCKTON
114 E. MARKET ST., WARRENSBURG, MO

DR. JAMES BRENT
1005 HIGHWAY W, WARRENTON, MO

DR. CHRISTIAN WESSLING
23 N. GORE AVE., STE. 209, WEBSTER GROVES, MO

MONTANA

DR. SARAH B. LANE
P.O. BOX 540, ARLEE, MT

DR. MARGARET R. BEESON
328 GRAND AVE., BILLINGS, MT

DR. CHARLES STREETER
P.O. BOX 1479, BILLINGS, MT

DR. GARY A. STRONG
503 WICKS LN., BILLINGS, MT

DR. SYLVIA M. SEYMOUR
65 W. KAGY BLVD., STE. B, BOZEMAN, MT

DR. CURT G. KURTZ
300 N. WILLSON AVE., BOZEMAN, MT

DR. NANCY AGENES
1820 HARRISON AVE., BUTTE, MT

DR. WILLIAM CORFF
P.O. BOX 338, EMIGRANT, MT

DR. LAWRENCE POLLACK
P.O. BOX 946, GARDINER, MT

DR. LEXA LEE
600 CENTRAL AVE., STE. 18, GREAT FALLS, MT

DR. MONA MORSTEIN
519 9TH ST. S, GREAT FALLS, MT

DR. CHARLES H. STEELE
2509 7TH AVE. S, GREAT FALLS, MT

DR. HILLARY DAILEY
173 BLODGETT CAMP RD., HAMILTON, MT

DR. ELISABETH KIRCHOF
424 S. YELLOWSTONE ST., LIVINGSTON, MT

DR. SYLVIA SEYMOUR
117 E. CALLENDER ST., LIVINGSTON, MT

DR. NANCY DUNNE
218 E. FRONT ST., STE. 303, MISSOULA, MT

DR. KATHLEEN E. CARTER
900 S. FINLEY POINT RD., POLSON, MT

DR. RICHARD KAHLER
301 2ND ST. E., APT. 1D, WHITEFISH, MT

NEBRASKA

DR. RAYMOND M. BEACH
300 W. 23RD ST., FREMONT, NE

DR. KATHY HURLEY
2144 S. 49TH ST., OMAHA, NE

DR. EUGENE OLIVETO
8031 W. CENTER RD. STE. 208, OMAHA, NE

DR. JOHN D. ROEHRS
2566 SAINT MARYS AVE., OMAHA, NE

DR. OTIS W. MILLER
408 S. 14TH ST., ORD, NE

NEVADA

DR. JAMES HAMTAK
101 HOT SPRINGS RD., #6F, CARSON CITY, NV

DR. ROBERT MILNE
2501 GREEN VALLEY PKY., HENDERSON, NV

DR. DOUGLAS BRODIE
848 TANAGER ST., INCLINE VILLAGE, NV

DR. REED W. HYDE
2225 E. FLAMINGO RD., STE. 301, LAS VEGAS, NV

DR. STEVEN A. MOLPER
2280 MONTESSOURI ST., LAS VEGAS, NV

DR. ROBERT VANCE
801 S. RANCHO DR., STE. F2, LAS VEGAS, NV

DR. JOSEPH F. TANGREDI
650 SHADOW LN. STE. 12, LAS VEGAS, NV

DR. RICHARD BAKER
2200 S. RANCHO DR., LAS VEGAS, NV

DR. DANIEL F. ROYAL
3720 HOWARD HUGHES PKY., LAS VEGAS, NV

DR. JOANNE STEFANATOS
1325 VEGAS VALLEY DR., LAS VEGAS, NV

DR. ROBERT D. MILNE
2110 PINTO LN., LAS VEGAS, NV

DR. FRANK SHALLENBERGER
P.O. BOX 69, MINDEN, NV

DR. EUNICE TANG
290 BRINKBY AVE., RENO, NV

DR. YIWEN Y. TANG
2725 W. LAKE RIDGE SHRS., RENO, NV

DR. DAVID A. EDWARDS
6490 S. McCARRAN BLVD., #C24, RENO, NV

DR. CORAZON M. IIARINA
6490 S. McCARRAN BLVD., #C24, RENO, NV

DR. W. J. DIAMOND
4600 KIETZKE LN., STE. M-242, RENO, NV

DR. DONALD E. SOLI
708 N. CENTER ST., RENO, NV

DR. MICHAEL L. GERBER
3670 GRANT DR., RENO, NV

NEW HAMPSHIRE

DR. PAMELA HERRING
46 S. MAIN ST., CONCORD, NH

DR. ROBERT TIMBERLAKE
66 N. STATE ST., CONCORD, NH

DR. MICHELE MOORE
115 KEY RD., KEENE, NH

DR. LEON HECHT
500 MARKET ST., STE. 1F, PORTSMOUTH, NH

DR. DEVRA KRASSNER
402 STATE ST., PORTSMOUTH, NH

NEW JERSEY

DR. PRATAP C. SINGHAL
431 WASHINGTON AVE., BELLEVILLE, NJ

DR. MURALIDHAR REDDY
234 GREENWICH ST., BELVIDERE, NJ

DR. ALLAN MAGAZINER
1907 GREENTREE RD., CHERRY HILL, NJ

DR. MAJID ALI
95 E. MAIN ST., DENVILLE, NJ

DR. JACK LARMER
34 BUSSELL CT., DUMONT, NJ

DR. EDWIN HELENIAK
811 MADISON AVE., DUNELLEN, NJ

DR. PAUL GILBERT
123 DUNHAMS CORNER RD., EAST BRUNSWICK, NJ

DR. C. Y. LEE
952 AMBOY AVE., EDISON, NJ

DR. RICHARD MENASHE
15 S. MAIN ST., EDISON, NJ

DR. MURALIDHAR REDDY
29 MARKHAM DR., LONG VALLEY, NJ

DR. CHARLES H. MINTZ
10 E. BROAD ST., MILLVILLE, NJ

DR. MONROE S. KARETZKY
201 LYONS AVE., NEWARK, NJ

DR. URSULA SZPRYT
17 LATHAM CIR., PARLIN, NJ

DR. PHILIP L. BONNET
114 W. FRANKLIN AVE., PENNINGTON, NJ

DR. JOSEPHINE L. SANTILLO
P.O. BOX 14, POMPTON PLAINS, NJ

DR. ERIC BRAVERMAN
212 COMMONS WAY, BLDG. 2, PRINCETON, NJ

DR. CONSTANCE ALFANO
74 OAK ST., RIDGEWOOD, NJ

DR. CHARLES HARRIS
1 ORTLEY PLAZA, SEASIDE HEIGHTS, NJ

DR. MARC CONDREN
15 CEDAR GROVE LN., #20, SOMERSET, NJ

DR. FRANK DICHIARA
2446 CHURCH RD., TOMS RIVER, NJ

DR. HERBERT FICHMAN
141 GANTTOWN RD., TURNERSVILLE, NJ

DR. JAMES F. CLAIRE
1600 S. BURNT MILL RD., VOORHEES, NJ

DR. SIDNEY B. SHANE
746 VALLEY RD., WAYNE, NJ

DR. FAINA MUNITO
51 PLEASANT VALLEY WAY, WEST ORANGE, NJ

NEW MEXICO

DR. JOSEPH COLLINS
P.O. BOX 44, ALAMOGORDO, NM

DR. HAROLD A. COHEN
6 WIND RD. N.W., ALBUQUERQUE, NM

DR. VASANT LAD
1231 SETTER DR. N.E., ALBUQUERQUE, NM

DR. LAUREN I. LEVICK
9204 MONTGOMERY BLVD. N.E., ALBUQUERQUE, NM

DR. WOLFGANG SCHMIDT-NOWARA
4775 INDIAN SCHOOL RD. N.E., ALBUQUERQUE, NM

DR. MARIANNE CALVANESSE
1612 HENDOLA DR. N.E., ALBUQUERQUE, NM

DR. GERALD PARKER
6208 MONTGOMERY BLVD. N.E., ALBUQUERQUE, NM

DR. JOHN T. TAYLOR
6208 MONTGOMERY BLVD. N.E., ALBUQUERQUE, NM

DR. DIANE H. POLASKY
540 CHAMA ST. N.E., STE. 9, ALBUQUERQUE, NM

DR. MARY A. COOPER
204 CARLISLE BLVD. N.E., ALBUQUERQUE, NM

DR. GERALD A. MONTGOMERY
800 ENCINO PL. N.E., #34, ALBUQUERQUE, NM

DR. KARL ROBINSON
1420 COLUMBIA DR. N.E., ALBUQUERQUE, NM

DR. DONNA L. DEMING
120 ALISO DR. S.E., ALBUQUERQUE, NM

DR. RALPH J. LUCIANI
2301 SAN PEDRO DR. N.E., STE. G, ALBUQUERQUE, NM

DR. DANIEL J. DIXON
P.O. BOX 28, ARROYO SECO, NM

DR. ERVIN DAILEY
P.O. BOX 1800, FARMINGTON, NM

DR. NORMAN HARRISON
1001 E. BOUTZ RD., LAS CRUCES, NM

DR. JACQUELYN KROHN
3917 WEST RD., LOS ALAMOS, NM

DR. LORENA C. ONDA
3 CALLE TARADDEI, #B, PLACITAS, NM

DR. E. L. MILLER
401 S. AVENUE A, PORTALES, NM

DR. ANNETTE STOESSER
112 S. KENTUCKY AVE., ROSWELL, NM

DR. ABBATE S. GARDNER
712 W. SAN MATEO RD., SANTA FE, NM

DR. GOVINDHA MCROSTIE
1468 S. SAINT FRANCIS DR., SANTA FE, NM

DR. DAMON FAZIO
2491 SAWMILL RD., APT. 1602, SANTA FE, NM

DR. SUSAN KREITZBERG
1404 2ND ST., SANTA FE, NM

DR. DON LEATHERS
1404 2ND ST,, SANTA FE, NM

DR. DAVID FRAWLEY
P.O. BOX 8357, SANTA FE, NM

DR. MARY L. MERRILL
P.O. BOX 1862, SANTA FE, NM

DR. BOB FREIDMAN
P.O. BOX 23526, SANTA FE, NM

DR. WILLARD H. DEAN
912 BACA ST., SANTA FE, NM

DR. WEST J. SHRADER
141 PASEO DE PERALTA, STE. A, SANTA FE, NM

DR. STEPHEN P. WEISS
1411 2ND ST., SANTA FE, NM

DR. DIETRICH KLINGHART
1468 S. SAINT FRANCIS DR., SANTA FE, NM

DR. SARAH C. RINGDAHL
501 FRANKLIN AVE., SANTA FE, NM

DR. JOAN KIRK
P.O. BOX 1661, TAOS, NM

NEW YORK

DR. AARON E. SHER
25 HACKETT BLVD., ALBANY, NY

DR. LARRY MALERBA
P.O. BOX 588A, ALTAMONT, NY

DR. JOSEPH D. BEASLEY
221 BROADWAY., STE. 303, AMITYVILLE, NY

DR. MAURICE KOUGUELL
997 CLINTON PL., BALDWIN, NY

DR. JANET MILLER
25 4TH AVE., BAY SHORE, NY

DR. JAMES M. MILLER
40 FRONT ST., BINGHAMTON, NY

DR. JACK COOPER
2 MARVIN AVE., BREWSTER, NY

DR. ROBERT ABBRUZZESE
141 N. STATE RD., BRIARCLIFF MANOR, NY

DR. RICHARD IZQUIERDO
1070 SOUTHERN BLVD., BRONX, NY

DR. JOSEPH S. WOJCIK
525 BRONXVILLE RD., APT. 1G, BRONXVILLE, NY

DR. FRANK NOCHIMSON
36 72ND ST., BROOKLYN, NY

DR. HAROLD WEISS
8002 19TH AVE., BROOKLYN, NY

DR. RICHARD SCHWIMMER
2635 NOSTRAND AVE., BROOKLYN, NY

DR. PAVEL YUTSIS
1309 W. 7TH ST., BROOKLYN, NY

DR. VICTORIA ZUPA
179 BERKELEY PL., BROOKLYN, NY

DR. GENNARO LOCURCIO
2386 OCEAN PKY., BROOKLYN, NY

DR. MICHAEL TEPLITSKY
415 OCEAN VIEW AVE., BROOKLYN, NY

DR. I-TSU CHAO
1641 E. 18TH ST., BROOKLYN, NY

DR. CARMINE ESPOSITO
3021 QUENTIN RD., BROOKLYN, NY

DR. EDWIN J. MANNING
3 GATES CIR., BUFFALO, NY

DR. KALPANA D. PATEL
191 NORTH ST., BUFFALO, NY

DR. DORIS J. RAPP
1421 COLVIN BLVD., BUFFALO, NY

DR. RAMIREZ-PRESTAS
P.O. BOX 5, CANDOR, NY

DR. KENNETH TARSIA
122 JEFFERSON HTS., CATSKILL, NY

DR. LEONARD VENEZIA
283 COMMACK RD., COMMACK, NY

DR. EDWIN SCHWARZ
196 S. CONGER AVE., CONGERS, NY

DR. CHRISTOPHE CALAPAI
1900 HEMPSTEAD TPKE., EAST MEADOW, NY

DR. LYNN MILLER
605 FRANKLIN PARK DR., EAST SYRACUSE, NY

DR. REINO HILL
230. W MAIN ST., FALCONER, NY

DR. JOHN RUPOLO
148 TULIP AVE., FLORAL PARK, NY

DR. MARJORIE S. SIEBERT
7309 MYRTLE AVE., FLUSHING, NY

DR. SERGE NERLI
59-11 161ST ST., FLUSHING, NY

DR. HENRY RUBANEK
110-28 70TH RD., FLUSHING, NY

DR. DEBORAH TURNER
8402 51ST AVE., FLUSHING, NY

DR. JOHN CRESCIOINE
877 STEWART AVE., STE. 15, GARDEN CITY, NY

DR. ANTHONY D. CAPOBIANCO
20 LANDING RD., GLEN COVE, NY

DR. TOBIAS J. YARYORA
935 NORTHERN BLVD., GREAT NECK, NY

DR. SERAFINA CORSELLO
175 E. MAIN ST., HUNTINGTON, NY

DR. IRVING LINKOFF
17215 HILLSIDE AVE., JAMAICA, NY

DR. ALFRED V. ZAMM
111 MAIDEN LN., KINGSTON, NY

DR. GERARD D. O'GRADY
7 MORICHES RD., LAKE GROVE, NY

DR. LUCY VAUGHTERS
571 RIDGE RD., LANSING, NY

DR. CHARLES BILLER
22 BEACH AVE., LARCHMONT, NY

DR. MITCHELL KURK
310 BROADWAY, LAWRENCE, NY

DR. ANTHONY LAZZARINO
130 S. 5TH ST., LEWISTON, NY

DR. PETER KASE
444 DAVISON RD., LOCKPORT, NY

DR. VICTOR LEVONSON
355 E. PARK AVE., LONG BEACH, NY

DR. MICHELLE COHEN
527 W. PARK AVE., LONG BEACH, NY

DR. DANIEL W. SQUILLANTY
4526 40TH ST., LONG ISLAND CITY, NY

DR. GREGORY BARK
5550 MERRICK RD., MASSAPEQUA, NY

DR. BOB SNIDER
HC 61 BOX 43D, MASSENA, NY

DR. ROBERT SNIDER
HC 61 BOX 43D, MASSENA, NY

DR. STEVEN FEINSILVER
222 STATION PLAZA N., MINEOLA, NY

DR. MICHAEL B. GALANTE
127 ROUTE 59, MONSEY, NY

DR. SUN F. PEI
1 FAIRFIELD LN., NEW HYDE PARK, NY

DR. ALLAN WARSHOWSKY
2001 MARCUS AVE., NEW HYDE PARK, NY

DR. MARTIN P. GOLDMAN
838 PELHAMDALE AVE., NEW ROCHELLE, NY

DR. RONALD HOFFMAN
40 E. 30TH ST., NEW YORK, NY

DR. WARREN LEVIN
444 PARK AVE. S,. NEW YORK, NY

DR. ROBERT C. ATKINS
152 E. 55TH ST., NEW YORK, NY

DR. ROBERT J. GORMLEY
638 9TH ST., NIAGARA FALLS, NY

DR. PAUL CUTLER
652 ELMWOOD AVE., NIAGARA FALLS, NY

DR. TERENCE DULIN
735 OLD BETHPAGE RD., OLD BETHPAGE, NY

DR. RICHARD J. UCCI
521 MAIN ST., ONEONTA, NY

DR. NEIL L. BLOCK
60 DUTCH HILL RD., ORANGEBURG, NY

DR. ROBERT MONK
100 S. HIGHLAND AVE., OSSINING, NY

DR. KENNETH A. BOCK
108 MONTGOMERY ST., RHINEBECK, NY

DR. BEN H. PARK
1576 LONG POND RD., ROCHESTER, NY

DR. DONALD W. GREENBLATT
2110 CLINTON AVE. S., ROCHESTER, NY

DR. MARTIN H. JENZER
1589 RIDGE RD. W., ROCHESTER, NY

DR. BARRY HEFFRON
410 LAKEVIEW AVE., ROCKVILLE CENTRE, NY

DR. TOVAH FINMAN
150 THEODORE FREMD AVE., RYE, NY

DR. PATRICIA ZEBREE
728 SWAGGERTOWN RD., SCHENECTADY, NY

DR. ROBERT A. WEISSBERG
P.O. BOX 9070, SCHENECTADY, NY

DR. HOWARD BLUM
1141 CRESTLINE PL., SEAFORD, NY

DR. MAXIMO C. CHULA
373 ROUTE 111, SMITHTOWN, NY

DR. MICHAEL R. GLASS
285 VANETTEN RD., SPENCER, NY

DR. PAUL SCHARFF
219 HUNGRY HOLLOW RD., SPRING VALLEY, NY

DR. ALFREDO LOPEZ DEL CASTI
126 WIELAND AVE., STATEN ISLAND, NY

DR. PENNY GOLDSTEIN
3932 HYLAN BLVD,, STATEN ISLAND, NY

DR. IRVING LINKOFF
1452 STONY BROOK RD., STONY BROOK, NY

DR. MICHAEL SCHACHFER
2 EXECUTIVE BLVD., SUFFERN, NY

DR. STEVEN SCHENKMAN
6801 JERICHO TPKE., SYOSSET, NY

DR. KAREN PICONE
6801 JERICHO TPKE., SYOSSET, NY

DR. JULIA BYRD
6801 JERICHO TPKE., SYOSSET, NY

DR. MARIAN WITTINK
6801 JERICHO TPKE., SYOSSET, NY

DR. EDWARD T. DOWNING
301 PROSPECT AVE., SYRACUSE, NY

DR. ROBERT E. WESTLAKE
BROAD RD., SYRACUSE, NY

DR. THERESE A. OSBORNE
406 FULTON ST., STE. 220, TROY, NY

DR. GEORGE PIZZO
188 BELMONT AVE., WEST BABYLON, NY

DR. TIMOTHY CARNEY
180 GREAT EAST NECK RD., WEST BABYLON, NY

DR. SAVELY YURKOVSKY
309 MADISON ST., WESTBURY, NY

DR. FREDERIC J. VAGNINI
1600 STEWART AVE., WESTBURY, NY

DR. CHARLES POLLAK
21 BLOOMINGDALE RD., WHITE PLAINS, NY

DR. STANLEY WEINDORF
75 FROEHLICH FARM BLVD., WOODBURY, NY

NORTH CAROLINA

DR. KEITH E. JOHNSON
188 QUEWHIFFLE RD., ABERDEEN, NC

DR. CHARLES E. WILEY
P.O. BOX 307, BANNER ELK, NC

DR. ROBERT KLINGENSMITH
RR 1 BOX 354B, BANNER ELK, NC

DR. PAUL SALE
P.O. BOX 640, BRYSON CITY, NC

DR. LOGAN ROBERTSON
RR 2, CANTON, NC

DR. ROBERT COLLIER
104 E. 7TH AVE., CHADBOURN, NC

DR. FRANCIS M. CARROLL
104 E. 7TH AVE., CHADBOURN, NC

DR. SHARON KING
109 CONNER DR., STE. 2102, CHAPEL HILL, NC

DR. F. K. DICKSON
485 N. WENDOVER RD., CHARLOTTE, NC

DR. DENNIS L. HILL
P.O. BOX 560727, CHARLOTTE, NC

DR. TIMOTHY HOLCOMB
1804 W. CUMBERLAND ST., DUNN, NC

DR. JAMES O. McNAMARA
P.O. BOX 2905, DURHAM, NC

DR. CONNIE WILSON
206 NESBITT CHAPEL RD., FAIRVIEW, NC

DR. CLINTON D. YOUNG
1200 N. ELM ST., GREENSBORO, NC

DR. JOHN L. LAIRD
RR 1, BOX 7, LEICESTER, NC

DR. JOHN L. WILSON
RR 1, BOX 7, LEICESTER, NC

DR. ROBERT COLLIER
3100 AILEEN DR., APT. D, RALEIGH, NC

DR. BHASKAR D. POWER
P.O. BOX 1132, ROANOKE RAPIDS, NC

DR. JOHN PITTMAN
1006 WEBB RD., SALISBURY, NC

DR. RICHARD W. ADAMS
700 HARTNESS RD., STATESVILLE, NC

DR. PHILLIP BICKERS
128 HEN RD., STONEVILLE, NC

DR. WALTER C. HOLLOWAY
P.O. BOX 380, WILKESBORO, NC

DR. TODD A. SMITH
P.O. BOX 24506, WINSTON SALEM, NC

DR. RICHARD D. BEY
160 CHARLOIS BLVD., WINSTON SALEM, NC

DR. J. B. SMITH, III
160 CHARLOIS BLVD., WINSTON SALEM, NC

DR. WALTER WARD
1411B PLAZA DR., WINSTON SALEM, NC

NORTH DAKOTA

DR. GALEN J. EACH
1432 4TH ST. N., FARGO, ND

DR. RICHARD H. LEIGH
2314 LIBRARY CIR., GRAND FORKS, ND

DR. LOUIS M. SILVERMAN
1000 S. COLUMBIA RD., GRAND FORKS, ND

OHIO

DR. JOSEPHINE ARONICA
1867 W. MARKET ST., AKRON, OH

DR. STOYAN P. DASKALOV
1613 S. LIBERTY AVE., ALLIANCE, OH

DR. L. T. CHAPPELL
122 THURMAN ST., BLUFFTON, OH

DR. RAYMOND S. ROSEDALE, JR.
4150 BELDEN VILLAGE ST. N.W., CANTON, OH

DR. EDWARD B. ALLMON
3560 WESTMORELAND RD. N.W., CANTON, OH

DR. JACK E. SLINGLUFF
5850 FULTON DR. N.W., CANTON, OH

DR. ARTHUR GARDIKES
7076 CORPORATE WAY, CENTERVILLE, OH

DR. JOHN H. BOYLES JR
7076 CORPORATE WAY, CENTERVILLE, OH

DR. HEATHER MORGAN
138 S. MAIN ST., CENTERVILLE, OH

DR. MARTIN B. SCHARF
1275 E. KEMPER RD., CINCINNATI, OH

DR. TED COLE
9678 CINCINNATI COLUMBUS RD., CINCINNATI, OH

DR. KAUSHAI K. BHARDWAJ
8325 COLERAIN AVE., CINCINNATI, OH

DR. DAVID C. FABREY
800 COMPTON RD., CINCINNATI, OH

DR. MILTON KRAMER
619 OAK ST., CINCINNATI, OH

DR. LEE BROOKS
2101 ADELBERT RD., CLEVELAND, OH

DR. DOUGLAS C. WEEKS
24700 CENTER RIDGE RD., CLEVELAND, OH

DR. JOHN BARON
4807 ROCKSIDE RD., STE. 100, CLEVELAND, OH

DR. JAMES P. FRANCKELTON
24700 CENTER RIDGE RD., CLEVELAND, OH

DR. DENIS GORGES
6837 PEARL RD., CLEVELAND, OH

DR. DUDLEY S. DINNER
9500 EUCLID AVE. #S53, CLEVELAND, OH

DR. GREGORY D. SEELEY
1940 E. 6TH ST., CLEVELAND, OH

DR. WILLIAM J. CATES
2885 W. DUBLIN GRANVILLE RD., COLUMBUS, OH

DR. KEVIN K. GRANGER
6010 E. MAIN ST., COLUMBUS, OH

DR. WILLIAM D. MITCHELL
3520 SNOUFFER RD., COLUMBUS, OH

DR. ERNEST SHEARER
4191 N. HIGH ST., COLUMBUS, OH

DR. MIKEL LYDY
1329 COUNTY LINE RD., CRESTLINE, OH

DR. MICHAEL C. GARN
275 GRAHAM RD., STE. 1, CUYAHOGA FALLS, OH

DR. RICHARD F. BAHR
2353 W. STROOP RD., DAYTON, OH

DR. DONALD E. FRICKE
513 E. STROOP RD., DAYTON, OH

DR. DAVID D. GOLDBERG
100 FOREST PARK DR., DAYTON, OH

DR. JAMES GRAHAM
1 WYOMING ST., STE. G-200, DAYTON, OH

DR. BURL MORRIS
P.O. BOX 364, DELPHOS, OH

DR. BETTY PALMER
4975 BRADENTON AVE., DUBLIN, OH

DR. WILLIAM J. CATES
6035 MEMORIAL DR., DUBLIN, OH

DR. HELMUT S. SCHMIDT
4975 BRADENTON AVE., DUBLIN, OH

DR. WADE BOYLE
623 NEELY MANOR, EAST PALESTINE, OH

DR. STUART B. DATT
26300 EUCLID AVE., EUCLID, OH

DR. MARK CULLEN
15088 RUTH RD., GUYSVILLE, OH

DR. RICHARD E. THOMPSON
221 S. 6TH ST., IRONTON, OH

DR. PHILIP ROBBINS
131 PORTSMOUTH ST., JACKSON, OH

DR. DONNA ARAND
3535 SOUTHERN BLVD., KETTERING, OH

DR. ROBERT PAGE
110 N. MAPLE ST., LANCASTER, OH

DR. RICHARD KRABILL
6231 N. RIDGE RD., MADISON, OH

DR. ROBERT B. YOUNG
201 S. KIBLER ST., NEW WASHINGTON, OH

DR. WILLIAM PLIKERD
974 N. 21ST ST., NEWARK, OH

DR. CHARLES S. RESSEGER
P.O. BOX 374, NORWALK, OH

DR. JOHN W. RECHSTEINER
1116 S. LIMESTONE ST., SPRINGFIELD, OH

DR. JOSE E. SANCHEZ
2615 SUNSET BLVD., STEUBENVILLE, OH

DR. MARK DUMAS
602 W. SYLVANIA AVE., TOLEDO, OH

DR. FRANK O. HORTON, III
2142 N. COVE BLVD., TOLEDO, OH

DR. JOSEPH I. SHAFFER
2213 CHERRY ST., TOLEDO, OH

DR. CHARLES W. PLATT
552 S. WEST ST., VERSAILLES, OH

EVELYN WERN MEDICAL CENTER
P.O. BOX 1801, WARREN, OH

DR. GREGORY M. PITMAN
7908 CINCINNATI DAYTON RD., WEST CHESTER, OH

DR. DERRICK LONSDALE
24700 CENTER RIDGE RD., WESTLAKE, OH

DR. ALSTON M. QUILLIN
67 E. WILSON BRIDGE RD., WORTHINGTON, OH

DR. ESCARLITO U. SEVILLA
5437 MAHONING AVE., YOUNGSTOWN, OH

DR. JAMES VENTRESCO JR
3848 TIPPECANOE RD., YOUNGSTOWN, OH

OKLAHOMA

DR. JERALD M. GILBERT
7530 N.W. 23RD ST., BETHANY, OK

DR. WILLIAM PHILPOTT
17171 S.E. 29TH ST., CHOCTAW, OK

DR. V. J. CONRAD
1616 S. BOULEVARD ST., EDMOND, OK

DR. ROBERT E. FARROW
RR 5 BOX 243, EUFAULA, OK

DR. FRED LIPOVITCH
907 N.W. KINGSWOOD RD., LAWTON, OK

DR. RICHARD B. DAWSON
707 N.W. 13TH ST., OKLAHOMA CITY, OK

DR. JOHN L. DAVID III
3330 N.W. 56TH ST., STE. 602, OKLAHOMA CITY, OK

DR. CHARLES D. TAYLOR
3715 N. CLASSEN BLVD., OKLAHOMA CITY, OK

DR. SKOSKHI T. FARR
10101 S. WESTERN AVE., OKLAHOMA CITY, OK

DR. P. R. RIEMER
700 DENVER ST., PAWNEE, OK

DR. DONALD M. DUSHAY
4444 S. HARVARD AVE., STE. 100, TULSA, OK

DR. JOHN MERRIMAN
2325 S. HARVARD AVE., TULSA, OK

DR. RAY WEATHERS
1211 S. HARVARD AVE., #A, TULSA, OK

DR. A. J. GEIGER
111 JAMESON DR., WYNNEWOOD, OK

OREGON

DR. KARL E. HUMISTON
P.O. BOX 2035, ALBANY, OR

DR. ZANE GARD
2315 S.W. 198TH AVE., ALOHA, OR

DR. SHANDOR WEISS
238 E. MAIN ST., STE. E, ASHLAND, OR

DR. BENJAMIN W. STOTT
64 N. 3RD ST., ASHLAND, OR

DR. RICHARD M. KIRSCHNER
P.O. BOX 896, ASHLAND, OR

DR. RICHARD G. ROVIN
1090 ELKADER ST., ASHLAND, OR

DR. JAMES Z. SAID
610 ORCHARD ST., ASHLAND, OR

DR. JOY CRADDICK
1206 LINDA ST., ASHLAND, OR

DR. LINDA HERRICK
586 GLENWOOD DR., ASHLAND, OR

DR. JOHN A. GREEN, III
21267 HIGHWAY 99E N.E., AURORA, OR

DR. JUDY PEABODY
202 S. MAIN ST., BANKS, OR

DR. RAVINDER S. SAHNI
9570 S.W. BEAVERTON HILLSDALE, BEAVERTON, OR

DR. DAVID K. SHEFRIN
12525 S.W. 3RD ST., BEAVERTON, OR

DR. MITCHELL B. STARGROVE
4720 S.W. WATSON AVE., BEAVERTON, OR

DR. JOHN JEFFRIES
4280 S.W. 110TH AVE., BEAVERTON, OR

DR. JACK D. DAUGHERTY
12195 S.W. ALLEN BLVD., BEAVERTON, OR

DR. ROBERT SHERMAN
12801 S.W. JENKINS RD., STE. B, BEAVERTON, OR

DR. SHEILA MYERS
1850 N.E. 6TH ST., BEND, OR

DR. JIM WILKENS
477 N.E. GREENWOOD AVE., BEND, OR

DR. DAN MCCLEERY
404 N.E. GREENWOOD AVE., BEND, OR

DR. HOWARD J. REINGOLD
365 N.E. GREENWOOD AVE., STE. 3, BEND, OR

DR. WM M. IMMEL
537 N.W. WALL ST., STE. E, BEND, OR

DR. PREM S. DEV
101 N. GRANT ST., STE. 212, CANBY, OR

DR. CLARENCE W. CAMPBELL
P.O. BOX 744, CANYONVILLE, OR

DR. JOSEPH T. MORGAN
1750 THOMPSON RD., COOS BAY, OR

DR. ANDREW W. ELLIOTT
260 E. 15TH AVE., STE. F, EUGENE, OR

DR. ADRIENNE BORG-COMADURAN
74 E. 18TH AVE., STE. 12, EUGENE, OR

DR. PAUL E. DART
132 E. BROADWAY, STE. 332, EUGENE, OR

DR. STEHANIE D. STORY
244 W. 12TH AVE., EUGENE, OR

DR. STEPHEN A. MESSER
400 E. 2ND AVE., STE. 105, EUGENE, OR

DR. ROBERT TEARSE
P.O. BOX 10905, EUGENE, OR

DR. DEBRA L. MARTIN-BELLEVIL
1185 ARTHUR ST., EUGENE, OR

DR. RODNEY SCHAFFER
400 E. 2ND AVE., STE. 105, EUGENE, OR

DR. ERICH FLEISCHAAN
120 N.E. MANZANITA AVE., GRANTS PASS, OR

DR. JAMES FITZSIMMONS, JR.
591 HIDDEN VALLEY RD., GRANTS PASS, OR

DR. DANIEL YOUNG
21328 S.E. ALDER CT., GRESHAM, OR

DR. ANDY CAMPBELL
1217 N.E. BURNSIDE ST., STE. 701, GRESHAM, OR

DR. KEVIN C. WILSON
1049 S.W. BASELINE RD., STE. 310, HILLSBORO, OR

DR. MELINDA CATOR
264 N.E. 3RD AVE., HILLSBORO, OR

DR. RICHARD NOBLE
1049 S.W. BASELINE RD., STE. 310, HILLSBORO, OR

DR. ROBERT J. SCHWARTZ
1237 STATE ST., HOOD RIVER, OR

DR. JOAN LAURANCE
209 OAK ST., HOOD RIVER, OR

DR. ANNA MACINTOSH
545 1ST ST., LAKE OSWEGO, OR

DR. SALLY LAMONT
560 1ST ST., STE. 204, LAKE OSWEGO, OR

DR. K. RIFKIN
338 2ND ST., LAKE OSWEGO, OR

DR. LARRY HERDENER
415 E. 3RD ST., McMINNVILLE, OR

DR. ERIC OVERLAND
2825 E. BARNETT RD., MEDFORD, OR

DR. CAROL PETHERBRIDGE
1603 E. BARNETT RD., MEDFORD, OR

DR. PATRICK K. DONOHOE
1603 E. BARNETT RD., MEDFORD, OR

DR. RALPH R. WEISS
121 GENESSEE ST., MEDFORD, OR

DR. A. KADISH
1012 E. JACKSON ST., MEDFORD, OR

DR. EDWARD M. GELLER
1744 E. McANDREWS RD., STE. A, MEDFORD, OR

DR. DURR ELMORE
14653 S. GRAVES RD., MULINO, OR

DR. JAMES W. FITZSIMMONS
P.O. BOX 130, MURPHY, OR

DR. ALICE DUNCAN
P.O. BOX 411, NESKOWIN, OR

DR. STEVEN ARVIDSON
1421 ARABIAN CT., NEWBERG, OR

DR. GERALD BROUHARD
1860 VIRGINIA AVE., NORTH BEND, OR

DR. NORA J. TALLMAN
10360 N.E. WASCO ST., PORTLAND, OR

DR. EDYTHE VICKERS
2348 N.W. LOVEJOY ST., PORTLAND, OR

DR. ADAM LADD
320 N.E. 120TH AVE., PORTLAND, OR

DR. DAVID A. GREENWPAN
11810 S.W. KING JAMES PL., PORTLAND, OR

DR. JAMES B. MASSEY
3285 S.W. 78TH AVE., PORTLAND, OR

DR. LEIA MELEAD
1405 N.E. BROADWAY ST., PORTLAND, OR

DR. SUZANNE SCOPES
316 N.E. 28TH AVE., PORTLAND, OR

DR. BARBARA B. JOLLEY
748 S.E. 181ST AVE., PORTLAND, OR

DR. JOHN SHERMAN
11231 S.E. MARKET ST., PORTLAND, OR

DR. SHAROL M. TILGNER
3427 N.E. 72ND AVE., PORTLAND, OR

DR. TORI HUDSON
11231 S.E. MARKET ST, PORTLAND, OR

DR. DAVID MACALLAN
P.O. BOX 16224, PORTLAND, OR

DR. JONNA R. ALEXANDER
635 N.E. 78TH AVE., PORTLAND, OR

DR. MARTIN MILNER
2104 N.E. 45TH AVE., #103, PORTLAND, OR

DR. STEVEN BAILEY
2606 N.W. VAUGHN ST., PORTLAND, OR

DR. JO JENNER
1514 S.E. TAYLOR ST., PORTLAND, OR

DR. LOUIS LIBBY
4805 N.E. GLISAN ST, PORTLAND, OR

DR. DONALD C. METTLER
2525 N.W. LOVEJOY ST., STE. 205, PORTLAND, OR

DR. HILARY FARBEROW
1330 S.E. 39TH AVE., PORTLAND, OR

DR. ROBERT SKLOVSKY
6910 S.E. LAKE RD., PORTLAND, OR

DR. JOSEPH J. COLETTO
10525 S.E. CHERRY BLOSSOM DR., PORTLAND, OR

DR. MARY F. CASELLI
2348 N.W. LOVEJOY ST., PORTLAND, OR

DR. JACQUELINE ROBERTS
7303 S.E. BROOKLYN ST., PORTLAND, OR

DR. MEREDITH L. LOWRY
5909 S.E. DIVISION ST., PORTLAND, OR

DR. DONALD C. WALKER
3619 S.E. DIVISION ST., PORTLAND, OR

DR. STEPHEN P. AUSTIN
3207 S.E. 25TH AVE., PORTLAND, OR

DR. SUSAN M. ROBERTS
4444 S.W. CORBETT AVE., PORTLAND, OR

DR. JOHN G. COLLINS
800 S.E. 181ST AVE., PORTLAND, OR

DR. BRUCE L. CANVASSR
805 S.E. SHERMAN ST., PORTLAND, OR

DR. JAMES R. PATTERSON
4805 N.E. GLISAN ST, PORTLAND, OR

DR. PATRICIA TIMBERLAKE
2625 S.E. HAWTHORNE BLVD., PORTLAND, OR

DR. RUSSELL B. MARZ
2002 S.E. 50TH AVE., PORTLAND, OR

DR. ANDREA SMITH
1614 S.E. 38TH AVE., PORTLAND, OR

DR. THOMAS L. ABSHIER
2615 S.E. 111TH AVE., APT. 4, PORTLAND, OR

DR. LOWELL M. CHODOSH
17068 S.E. MCLOUGHLIN BLVD., PORTLAND, OR

DR. PAMELA S. JEANNE
800 S.E. 181ST AVE., PORTLAND, OR

DR. THOMAS A. KURZEL
800 S.E. 181ST AVE., PORTLAND, OR

DR. CATHERINE STAUBER
10543 N.E. THOMPSON ST., PORTLAND, OR

DR. KEVON ARTHURS
2223 S.E. 114TH PL., PORTLAND, OR

DR. RITA BETTENBURG
10360 N.E. WASCO ST., PORTLAND, OR

DR. DEBORAH P. BARRETT
6132 S.E. YAMHILL ST., PORTLAND, OR

DR. ARN STRASSER
2050 N.W. LOVEJOY ST., #2, PORTLAND, OR

DR. GERALD B. RICH
1130 N.W. 22ND AVE., STE. 240, PORTLAND, OR

DR. RICHARD BARRETT
6132 S.E. YAMHILL ST., PORTLAND, OR

DR. DAVID A. HINTON
3074 LANCASTER DR. N.E., #205, SALEM, OR

DR. STEPHEN ALBIN
1880 LANCASTER DR. N.E., #109, SALEM, OR

DR. TERENCE H. YOUNG
1205 WALLACE RD. N.W., SALEM, OR

DR. ALEX SERKALOW
665 12TH ST. S.E., SALEM, OR

DR. ANDREW M. PERRY
410 LANCASTER DR. N.E., STE. B, SALEM OR

DR. EDWARD K. ALSTAT
14385 S.E. LUSTED RD., SANDY, OR

DR. RICHARD M. BRINKMAN
4320 CALAROGA DR., WEST LINN, OR

DR. MICHAEL JACOBS
P.O. BOX 497, WILSONVILLE, OR

PENNSYLVANIA

DR. JOHN V. CAPPELLO
5930 HAMILTON BLVD., ALLENTOWN, PA

DR. NICHOLAS E. WISNIEWSKI
4084 MT. ROYAL BLVD., #107, ALLISON PARK, PA

MEDICAL AND DENTAL CENTER
111 BALA AVE., BALA CYNWYD, PA

DR. BILL ILLINGWORTH
120 W. JOHN ST., BEDFORD, PA

DR. ROBERT STASHKO
110 SCANLON ST., BERWICK, PA

DR. SALLY A. REX
1343 EASTON AVE., BETHLEHEM, PA

DR. W. W. SHAY
407 E. PHILADELPHIA AVE., BOYERTOWN, PA

DR. MICHAEL L. PAWK
210 N. WASHINGTON ST., BUTLER, PA

DR. BRIAN FREEMAN
3913 MARKET ST., CAMP HILL, PA

DR. NORMEN E. WENGER
P.O. BOX 502, CARBONDALE, PA

DR. MING P. MOLONY
101 BRIDGE ST., CATASAUQUA, PA

DR. ROBERT CUTRIGHT
1461 LINCOLN WAY E., CHAMBERSBURG, PA

DR. RONALD M. REPICE
1502 UPLAND ST., CHESTER, PA

DR. JAMES MAGEE
2615 N. BROAD ST., COLMAR, PA

DR. OLINDA FLORO
200 COMMERCE DR., CORAOPOLIS, PA

DR. RUSSELL FLACCO
573 N. MAIN ST., DOYLESTOWN, PA

DR. MICHAEL DIPALMA
58 E. OAKLAND AVE., DOYLESTOWN, PA

DR. DENNIS L. GILBERT
50 N. MARKET ST., ELIZABETHTOWN, PA

DR. CHIN Y. CHUNG
210 E. 2ND ST., ERIE, PA

DR. SIDNEY P. LIPMAN
225 W. 25TH ST., STE. 207, ERIE, PA

DR. MANTELL DONALD
6505 MARS RD., EVANS CITY, PA

DR. LESTER BLANK
1116 SIMMONTOWN RD., GAP, PA

DR. ALLAN BURATTI
13630 MOLLY PITCHER HWY., GREENCASTLE, PA

DR. RALPH A. MIRANDA
RR 12 BOX 108, GREENSBURG, PA

DR. ROY E. KERRY
17 6TH AVE., GREENVILLE, PA

DR. JAY YASGUR
P.O. BOX 925, GREENVILLE, PA

DR. RONALD BUNT
354 MAIN ST., HARLEYSVILLE, PA

DR. JOSEPH STUNCHULA
3690 VARTAN WAY, HARRISBURG, PA

DR. ROWENA DE-JESUS
RR 2 BOX P6B2, HAZLETON, PA

DR. ARTHUR L. KOCH
57 W. JUNIPER ST., HAZLETON, PA

DR. RICHARD PARCINSKI
1020 FRANKLIN ST., JOHNSTOWN, PA

DR. IRA S. CANTOR
P.O. BOX 447, KIMBERTON, PA

DR. RICHARD G. FRIED
P.O. BOX 447, KIMBERTON, PA

DR. GERALD REISINGER
6 GERSHOM PL., KINGSTON, PA

DR. BONNIE BECKER
P.O. BOX 409, KULPSVILLE, PA

DR. HENRY N WILLIAMS
556 W. JAMES ST., LANCASTER, PA

DR. RICHARD K. KOONS
1123 REINOEHL ST., LEBANON, PA

DR. GEORGE C. MILLER II
3 HOSPITAL DR., LEWISBURG, PA

DR. DAVID CROWLEY
5458 STEUBENVILLE PIKE, McKEES ROCKS, PA

DR. C. E. SHEAFFER
11 FLOWERS DR., MECHANICSBURG, PA

DR. MITCHEL E. SHAPIRO
6 ROYLENCROFT LN., MEDIA, PA

DR. CONRAD G. MAULFAIR, JR.
P.O. BOX 71, MERTZTOWN, PA

DR. KEVIN EMMONS
346 W. TRENTON AVE., MORRISVILLE, PA

DR. MAMDUH EL-ATTRACHE
20 E. MAIN ST., MOUNT PLEASANT, PA

DR. MICHAEL REECE
1065 W. MAIN ST., NEW HOLLAND, PA

DR. CHARLES COVERT
2936 AQUETONG RD., NEW HOPE, PA

DR. CLARENCE MONTA
61 REEDER RD., NEW HOPE, PA

DR. ROBERT J. PETERSON
64 MAGNOLIA DR., NEWTOWN, PA

DR. JACQUELINE RUSSELL
801 E. GERMANTOWN PIKE, NORRISTOWN, PA

DR. CARRIE COSSABOON
342 MEADOWBROOK RD., NORTH WALES, PA

DR. GREGG LODES
519 PAPER MILL RD., ORELAND, PA

DR. LANCE WRIGHT
3901 MARKET ST., PHILADELPHIA, PA

DR. RICHARD J. SCHWAB
3400 SPRUCE ST., #11, PHILADELPHIA, PA

DR. ALLAN I. PACK
3400 SPRUCE ST., #11, PHILADELPHIA, PA

DR. JUNE M. FRY
3200 HENRY AVE., PHILADELPHIA, PA

DR. JERRY E. THOMPSON
6161 CHESTNUT ST., PHILADELPHIA, PA

DR. KARL DOGHRAMJI
1015 WALNUT ST., PHILADELPHIA, PA

DR. DEBORAH McGREGOR
234 S. 22ND ST., PHILADELPHIA, PA

DR. NEIL COHEN
6850 OXFORD AVE., PHILADELPHIA, PA

DR. SHAUN KAVANAUGH
5001 OXFORD AVE., PHILADELPHIA, PA

DR. P. TAYALASHMI
6366 SHERWOOD RD., PHILADELPHIA, PA

DR. K. R. SAMPATHACHAR
6366 SHERWOOD RD., PHILADELPHIA, PA

DR. JESSE DE LA ROSA
333 W. MOUNT PLEASANT AVE., PHILADELPHIA, PA

DR. OWEN ROGAL
260 S. BROAD ST., PHILADELPHIA, PA

DR. P. JAYALAKSHMI
6366 SHERWOOD RD., PHILADELPHIA, PA

DR. MURA GALPERIN
824 HENDRIX ST., PHILADELPHIA, PA

DR. J. B. DOVBERG
1405 SNYDER AVE., PHILADELPHIA, PA

DR. LUCY NITSKANSKY
9369 HOFF ST., PHILADELPHIA, PA

DR. LEANDER T. ELLIS
2746 BELMONT AVE., PHILADELPHIA, PA

DR. ELYA SPIVAK
14425 BUSTLETON AVE., PHILADELPHIA, PA

DR. MARY L. BRADY
8712 FRANKFORD AVE., #1A, PHILADELPHIA, PA

DR. FREDERICK D. BURTON
1019 E. HAINES ST., PHILADELPHIA, PA

DR. RUSSELL FLACCO
12030 BUSTLETON AVE., PHILADELPHIA, PA

DR. CHERYL MONTELEONE
2315 PRIMROSE ST., PITTSBURGH, PA

DR. FRANNE R. BEREZ
1926 MURRAY AVE., PITTSBURGH, PA

DR. CHARLES F. REYNOLDS, III
3811 OHARA ST., PITTSBURGH, PA

DR. RODGER STEWART
2022 MOUNT TROY RD., STE. A, PITTSBURGH, PA

DR. ALAN BERMAN
4354 MURRAY AVE., PITTSBURGH, PA

DR. HELEN F. KRAUSE
9104 BABCOCK BLVD., PITTSBURGH, PA

DR. DAN ROYAL
937 LITTLE BRITAIN RD. N., QUARRYVILLE, PA

DR. EUGENE R. SHIPPEN
9 E. LANCASTER AVE., READING, PA

DR. S. RAMAKRISHNA
1822 MULBERRY ST., SCRANTON, PA

DR. JOHN F. MOYER, JR.
701 BROAD ST., SEWICKLEY, PA

DR. DAVID SCHRIER
1395 CHURCHVILLE RD., SOUTHAMPTON, PA

DR. BRUCE ROTHENBERGER
P.O. BOX 444, SPRING HOUSE, PA

DR. ROBERT INTERVAL
177 E. HIGH ST., WAYNESBURG, PA

DR. WILLET NEFF
608 EASTON RD., APT. B, WILLOW GROVE, PA

DR. STEVEN C. HALBERT
1442 ASHBOURNE RD., WYNCOTE, PA

DR. DONALD D. PETERSON
100 E. LANCASTER AVE., WYNNEWOOD, PA

PUERTO RICO

DR. JOSE R. ZARAGOZA
P.O. BOX 1028, ARECIBO, PR

DR. LUIS A. CHRISTIAN
P.O. BOX 877, JUANA DIAZ, PR

DR. EFRAIN R. MALAVE
571 CALLE LODI, SAN JUAN, PR

RHODE ISLAND

DR. MARY RADIO
137 HIGH SERVICE AVE., NORTH PROVIDENCE, RI

DR. MICHAEL ROSENBERG
207 WATERMAN AVE., NORTH PROVIDENCE, RI

DR. RICHARD P. MILLMAN
593 EDDY ST., PROVIDENCE, RI

SOUTH CAROLINA

DR. MAARTIN ZWERLING
P.O. BOX 2456, AIKEN, SC

DR. ANTHONY E. HARRIS
154 WATERLOO ST. S.W., AIKEN, SC

DR. GARY WICKISER
3618 E. RIVER ST., ANDERSON, SC

DR. HARRIET GRADY-THOMAS
P.O. BOX 60673, CHARLESTON, SC

DR. FREDDIE E. WILSON
701 GROVE RD., GREENVILLE, SC

DR. W. B. GRAY, III
446 GRACE ST., GREENWOOD, SC

DR. TERRY A. MARSHALL
1325 SPRING ST., GREENWOOD, SC

DR. THEODORE C. ROZEMA
1000 E. RUTHERFORD ST., LANDRUM, SC

DR. PAMELA KENNEDY
P.O. BOX 337, LANDRUM, SC

DR. ROCCO D. CASSONE
1175 COOK RD. N.E., STE. 230, ORANGEBURG, SC

DR. WILSON P. SMITH, JR.
101 E. WOOD ST., SPARTANBURG, SC

SOUTH DAKOTA

DR. ALAN JUEL
2902 W. MAIN ST., STE. 4, RAPID CITY, SD

DR. LARRY LYTLE
3312 JACKSON BLVD., RAPID CITY, SD

DR. K. A. KELTS
P.O. BOX 6000, RAPID CITY, SD

DR. RICHARD HARDIE
1100 S. EUCLID AVE., SIOUX FALLS, SD

TENNESSEE

DR. CALVIN P. BRYAN
3812 TENNESSEE AVE., CHATTANOOGA, TN

DR. MARK WILLIAMS
83 MOUSE CREEK RD. N.W., CLEVELAND, TN

DR. DARRELL WELLS
111 HAZEL PATH, HENDERSONVILLE, TN

DR. WILLIAM G. CROOK
681 SKYLINE DR., JACKSON, TN

DR. WILLIAM FINLEY
900 E. OAK HILL AVE., KNOXVILLE, TN

DR. THOMAS G. HIGGINS
1901 W. CLINCH AVE., KNOXVILLE, TN

DR. BERT A. HAMPTON
1901 W. CLINCH AVE., KNOXVILLE, TN

DR. FRED M. FURR
9217 PARK WEST BLVD. E., STE. 1, KNOXVILLE, TN

DR. NEAL AGUILLARD
1265 UNION AVE., #12, MEMPHIS, TN

DR. RICHARD G. WANDERMAN
5545 MURRAY RD., STE. 330, MEMPHIS, TN

DR. J. B. HAYNES, JR.
P.O. BOX 380, NASHVILLE, TN

DR. MARCI T. POE
2221 MURPHY AVE., NASHVILLE, TN

DR. STEPHEN L. REISMAN
28 WHITE BRIDGE RD., #400, NASHVILLE, TN

DR. CORINNE S. ROVETTI
2708 HAPPY CREEK RD., SEVIERVILLE, TN

DR. L. A. HORSTMANN
1815 PARKWAY, SEVIERVILLE, TN

TEXAS

DR. WILLIAM I. FOX
1227 N. MOCKINGBIRD LN., ABILENE, TX

DR. HERBERT CARR
P.O. BOX 1179, ALAMO, TX

DR. GERALD PARKER
4714 S. WESTERN ST., AMARILLO, TX

DR. JOHN T. TAYLOR
4714 S. WESTERN ST., AMARILLO, TX

DR. TERRY RUDD
3701 OLSEN BLVD., AMARILLO, TX

DR. A. L. KARBACH
316 N. CENTER ST., ARLINGTON, TX

DR. CHARLES R. HAMEL
4412 MATLOCK RD., STE. 300, ARLINGTON, TX

DR. ROBERT E. HAZELWOOD
1610 NORTHWOOD RD., AUSTIN, TX

DR. RUSSELL R. ROBY
3410 FAR WEST BLVD., STE. 110, AUSTIN, TX

DR. JAMES HEFFLEY
4111 MEDICAL PKY., AUSTIN, TX

DR. VLADIMAR RIZOV
8235 SHOAL CREEK BLVD., AUSTIN, TX

DR. HOWARD J. LANG
1404 BROWN TRL., BEDFORD, TX

DR. CHARLES R. CHUNG
1850 CENTRAL DR., BEDFORD, TX

DR. PETER E. ERICKSON
P.O. BOX 608, BOLING, TX

DR. CHARLES ROGERS
507 E. ELIZABETH ST., BROWNSVILLE, TX

DR. BARBARA ANGELL
1206 N. JOSEY LN., CARROLLTON, TX

DR. EDDIE HARRIS
1908 BRYAN ST., DALLAS, TX

DR. R. W. NOBLE
6757 ARAPAHO RD., STE. 757, DALLAS, TX

DR. BRIJ MYER
4222 TRINITY MILLS RD., #222, DALLAS, TX

DR. RALPH E. SMILEY
8345 WALNUT HILL LN., STE. 205, DALLAS, TX

DR. J. R. WINSLOW
2815 VALLEY VIEW LN., STE. 111, DALLAS, TX

DR. JAMES P. LOFTIN
P.O. BOX 819094, DALLAS, TX

DR. JOEL STEINBERG
1935 MOTOR ST., DALLAS, TX

DR. GERALD H. ROSS
8345 WALNUT HILL LN., STE. 205, DALLAS, TX

DR. WILLIAM REA
8345 WALNUT HILL LN., STE. 205, DALLAS, TX

DR. RICHARD G. JAECKLE
8220 WALNUT HILL LN., STE. 404, DALLAS, TX

DR. ANDREW O. JAMIESON
8200 WALNUT HILL LN., DALLAS, TX

DR. PHILIP M. BECKER
8200 WALNUT HILL LN., DALLAS, TX

DR. JOE D. GOLDSTRICH
8215 WESTCHESTER DR., STE. 307, DALLAS, TX

DR. GONZALO DIAZ
1801 N. OREGON ST., EL PASO, TX

DR. JOSEPH ARTEAGA
2001 N. OREGON ST., EL PASO, TX

INTERNATIONAL MEDICAL CENTER
424 EXECUTIVE CENTER BLVD., EL PASO, TX

DR. FRANCISCO SOTO
1420 GERONIMO DR., STE. D-2, EL PASO, TX

DR. GERALD HALL
10904 LAKEWOOD AVE., EL PASO, TX

DR. CHARLES A. RUSH, JR.
4351 BOOTH CALLOWAY RD., #105, FORT WORTH, TX

DR. JAMES C. WHITTINGTON
1021 7TH AVE., FORT WORTH, TX

DR. EDGAR LUCAS
1400 8TH AVE., FORT WORTH, TX

DR. D. W. BROWN, SR.
109 S. ADAMS ST., FREDERICKSBURG, TX

DR. DONALD W. BROOKS
2045 FOREST LN., STE. 140, GARLAND, TX

DR. PAUL P. SCHORR
328 W. INTERSTATE 30, GARLAND, TX

DR. GEORGE B. MARSH, JR.
P.O. BOX H, GRAND SALINE, TX

DR. CONSTANTIN A. KOTSANIS
1600 W. COLLEGE ST., GRAPEVINE, TX

DR. ROBERT D. HENLEY
163 ALDINE BENDER RD., HOUSTON, TX

DR. GILBERT MANSO
5177 RICHMOND AVE., STE. 125, HOUSTON, TX

DR. VICKEY HALLORAN
5629 FM 1960 RD. W., STE. 225, HOUSTON, TX

DR. JACOB SIEGEL
8300 WATERBURY DR., STE. 305, HOUSTON, TX

DR. TODD SWICK
8300 WATERBURY DR., STE. 350, HOUSTON, TX

DR. KARL ROBINSON
2370 RICE BLVD., HOUSTON, TX

DR. OWEN ROBINS
6565 DE MOSS DR., STE. 202, HOUSTON, TX

DR. ROBERT BATTLE
9910 LONG POINT RD., HOUSTON, TX

DR. JEROME L. BOROCHOFF
8830 LONG POINT RD. STE. 504, HOUSTON, TX

DR. KARL L. YANG
6411 FANNIN ST., HOUSTON, TX

VURZYNSKI RESEARCH INSTITUTE
12000 RICHMOND AVE. #260, HOUSTON, TX

DR. SELIC SOROKA
6206 DASHWOOD DR., HOUSTON, TX

DR. JOHN P. TROWBRIDGE
9816 MEMORIAL BLVD., STE. 205, HUMBLE, TX

DR. MICHAEL E. TRUMAN
1709 PRECINCT LINE RD., HURST, TX

DR. OSA J. OKUNDAYE
2618 N. BELT LINE RD., IRVING, TX

DR. SALVADOR FIGUEROA III
888 KINWEST PKY., APT. 46, IRVING, TX

DR. JOHN J. SESSIONS
1609 S. MARGARET AVE., KIRBYVILLE, TX

DR. R. M. DAVIS
10414 SPENCER HWY., LA PORTE, TX

DR. EVERETT P. STEWART
2232 INDIANA AVE., LUBBOCK, TX

DR. HARLAND O. WRIGHT
5009 UNIVERSITY AVE., LUBBOCK, TX

DR. JOHN G. ADAMS
711 E. END BLVD. S, MARSHALL, TX

DR. BILLY G. MILLS
4725 GUS THOMASSON RD., MESQUITE, TX

DR. NORMAN RALSTON
12500 LAKE JUNE RD., MESQUITE, TX

DR. JOE A. IZEN
3912 BROOKHAVEN AVE., PASADENA, TX

DR. LINDA MARTIN
1524 INDEPENDENCE PKY., PLANO, TX

DR. JACK TAYLOR
3749 39TH ST., PORT ARTHUR, TX

DR. ROY H. SCHMIDLI
228 W. MAIN ST., PORT LAVACA, TX

DR. ROBERT R. THORESON
405 OLD WEST DR., ROUND ROCK, TX

DR. JIM P. ARCHER
8434 FREDERICKSBURG RD., SAN ANTONIO, TX

DR. JOLYN ENGLISH
1946 LA MANDA BLVD., SAN ANTONIO, TX

DR. BILLIE SAHLEY
5282 MEDICAL DR., STE. 160, SAN ANTONIO, TX

DR. RON STOGRYN
7334 BLANCO RD., STE. 100, SAN ANTONIO, TX

DR. LAWRENCE M. COHEN
2515 MCCULLOUGH AVE., SAN ANTONIO, TX

DR. JODY GREEN
11901 TOEPPERWEIN RD., SAN ANTONIO, TX

DR. GEORGE W. HEUNERS
213 ELM ST., SEGUIN, TX

DR. PETER E. ERICKSON
6526 LOUETTA RD., SPRING, TX

DR. R. C. CHAMBERS
9914 HIGHWAY 90A, SUGAR LAND, TX

DR. ELISABETH A. COLE
303 N. McKINNEY ST., SWEENY, TX

DR. FRANCISCO PEREZ-GUERRA
240 S. 31ST ST., TEMPLE, TX

DR. MALCOLM C. MALEY
808 OLIVE ST., STE. C, TEXARKANA, TX

DR. CHARLES R. MABRAY
4204 N. LAURENT ST., VICTORIA, TX

DR. GEORGE CONSTANT
115 MEDICAL DR., STE. 201, VICTORIA, TX

DR. WILLIAM E. WAGNON, JR.
3500 HILLCREST DR., WACO, TX

UTAH

DR. DAVID J. HARBRECHT
425 MEDICAL DR., STE. 107, BOUNTIFUL, UT

DR. OAKLEY GORDON
69 N. GUIDELIGHT DR., CEDAR CITY, UT

DR. JOSEPH D. HANSEN
195 N. 200 E, LOGAN, UT

DR. WILLIAM A. NUNN
345 E. 4500 S., STE. H, MURRAY, UT

DR. LOUIS CARR
207 N. STATE ST., OREM, UT

DR. DENNIS REMINGTON
1675 N. FREEDOM BLVD., STE. 11E, PROVO, UT

DR. DENNIS D. HARPER
1675 N. FREEDOM BLVD., PROVO, UT

DR. ROBERT ARBON
777 N. 500 W., STE. 105, PROVO, UT

DR. GLENN L. EARL
644 S. 900 E., SALT LAKE CITY, UT

DR. ROBERT PAYNE
201 E. 5900 S., SALT LAKE CITY, UT

DR. WILLIAM A. NUNN
247 E. 900 S., SALT LAKE CITY, UT

DR. ROBERT J. FARNEY
325 8TH AVE., SALT LAKE CITY, UT

DR. GLEN JOHNSON
3540 S. 4000 W., STE. 130, WEST VALLEY CITY, UT

VERMONT

DR. FAIZI MEDEIROS
335 QUECHEE W. HARTFORD RD., WHITE RIVER, VT

DR. GEORGE GLANZBERG
RR 1, BOX 373, NORTH BENNINGTON, VT

DR. MARCEL HERNANDEZ
58 WESTERN AVE., BRATTLEBORO, VT

DR. JOHN R. ROOS
2 CHURCH ST., BURLINGTON, VT.

VIRGINIA

DR. ROGER D. NEAL
P.O. BOX 1328, ABINGDON, VA

DR. RICHARD D. FISHER
4222 EVERGREEN LN., ANNANDALE, VA

DR. SCOTT V. ANDERSON
7023 LITTLE RIVER TPKE., ANNANDALE, VA

DR. MITCHELL A. FLEISHER
RR 1 BOX 340, ARRINGTON, VA

DR. GEORGE A. GUESS
617 W. MAIN ST., STE. 5B, CHARLOTTESVILLE, VA

DR. J. JOSEPH
2430 MEADOWS LANDING, CHESAPEAKE, VA

DR. SANDRA M. CHASE
10418 WHITEHEAD ST., FAIRFAX, VA

DR. LINWOOD W. CUSTALOW
1832 TODDS LN., HAMPTON, VA

DR. HAROLD HUFFMAN
P.O. BOX 197, HINTON, VA

HEALTH DEVELOPMENT CENTER
9510 TECHNOLOGY DR., MANASSAS, VA

DR. SUSAN ZIMMER
P.O. BOX 495, MARSHALL, VA

DR. ERIC P. HARTMANN
1330 OLD CHAIN BRIDGE RD., McLEAN, VA

DR. HENRY PALACIOS
1481 CHAIN BRIDGE RD., McLEAN, VA

DR. PETER C. GENT
11900 HULL STREET RD., MIDLOTHIAN, VA

DR. KEITH JASSY
13730 MIDLOTHIAN TPKE., MIDLOTHIAN, VA

DR. REUBEN H. McBRAYER
600 GRESHAM DR., NORFOLK, VA

DR. VIRGIL WOOTEN
600 GRESHAM DR., NORFOLK, VA

DR. LAURIE BLACKWOOD
2121 TUCKAWAY LN., RICHMOND, VA

DR. GLEN M. GIESSEL
7101 JAHNKE RD., RICHMOND, VA

DR. SUE OSBORN
2925 ELLWOOD AVE., RICHMOND, VA

DR. WILLIAM S. ELIAS
P.O. BOX 12946, ROANOKE, VA

DR. RICHARD M. EVANS
5923 AUGUSTA DR., SPRINGFIELD, VA

DR. SAT-KARTAR K. KHALSA
20212 BROAD RUN DR., STERLING, VA

DR. ELMER M. CRANTON
P.O. BOX 44, TROUT DALE, VA

DR. BRENDAN STACK
8306A OLD COURTHOUSE RD., VIENNA, VA

DR. WATSON A. WALDEN
801 CEDAR CREEK GRADE, WINCHESTER, VA

WASHINGTON

DR. RUOS BORNEMAN
1004 7TH ST., ANACORTES, WA

DR. DEBRA CLAPP
1213 14TH ST., ANACORTES, WA

DR. MAGDA MISCHE
901 8TH ST., ANACORTES, WA

DR. IRENE D. SIMPSON
104 S. WEST AVE., ARLINGTON, WA

DR. JILL STANSBURY
506 E. MAIN ST., BATTLE GROUND, WA

DR. FRANK HOFFMAN
14866 N.E. 11TH PL., BELLEVUE, WA

DR. VIRENDER SODHI
10025 N.E. 4TH ST., BELLEVUE, WA

DR. ELIZABETH FREEMAN
10603 N.E. 14TH ST., BELLEVUE, WA

DR. DAVID BUSCHER
1370 116TH AVE. N.E., STE. 102, BELLEVUE, WA

DR. PAULA BARUFFI
13401 BEL RED RD., STE. A4, BELLEVUE, WA

DR. MICHAEL T. MURRAY
15401 S.E. 54TH CT., BELLEVUE, WA

DR. MARK W. STEINBERG
1919 BROADWAY, STE. 206, BELLINGHAM, WA

DR. PAUL GREENWOOD
1470 ELLIS ST., BELLINGHAM, WA

DR. MARGOT J. POSS
1155 N. STATE ST., BELLINGHAM, WA

DR. LAURA A. SHELTON
1321 KING ST., STE. 1, BELLINGHAM, WA

DR. V. J. WESSELS, JR.
1903 D ST., BELLINGHAM, WA

DR. MICHAEL ASHLEY
20611 BOTHELL EVERETT HWY., BOTHELL, WA

DR. CINDY BECK
107 N. TOWER AVE., STE. 5, CENTRALIA, WA

DR. H. R. HOBBS
4151 E. TARTAN WAY, CLINTON, WA

DR. STEVEN SANDBERG-LEWIS
P.O. BOX 493, EASTSOUND, WA

DR. RALPH W. WILSON
23700 EDMONDS WAY, STE. 102, EDMONDS, WA

DR. HENRY HOCHBERG
7935 216TH ST. S.W., STE. E, EDMONDS, WA

DR. JENNIFER JACOBS
23200 EDMONDS WAY, EDMONDS, WA

DR. DEAN CROTHERS
23200 EDMONDS WAY, EDMONDS, WA

DR. ANNE L. MAGUIRE
23405 84TH AVE. W., EDMONDS, WA

DR. HEATHER WOODS
5919 148TH ST. S.W., EDMONDS, WA

DR. CHERYL L. WOOD
7614 195TH ST. S.W., EDMONDS, WA

DR. NORMAN ZUCKER
700 S. 320TH ST., FEDERAL WAY, WA

DR. RAY H. KRUEGER
301 S. 320TH ST., FEDERAL WAY, WA

DR. KATE DATA
1404 54TH AVE. E,, FIFE, WA

DR. STEVEN W. DAVIS
6708A 144TH ST. N.W., GIG HARBOR, WA

DR. MARY GRIFFITH
6708 144TH ST. N.W., #A, GIG HARBOR, WA

DR. RHONDA G. SUMMERLAND
P.O. BOX 115, INDEX, WA

DR. DIRK W. POWELL
10725 S.E. 256TH ST., STE. 5, KENT, WA

DR. NORMAN ZUCKER
1872 CENTRAL PL. S., APT. H80, KENT, WA

DR. JONATHAN WRIGHT
24030 132ND AVE. S.E., KENT, WA

DR. SANDRA DENTON
24030 132ND AVE. S.E., KENT, WA

DR. DAVIS W. LAMSON
24030 132ND AVE. S.E., KENT, WA

DR. ROBERT M. MARTINEZ
903 5TH AVE., STE. 103A, KIRKLAND, WA

DR. DAVID BOVE
607 MARKET ST., KIRKLAND, WA

DR. SHEILA B. DUNN
607 MARKET ST., KIRKLAND, WA

DR. ROBERT L. GARRISON
143 PARK LN., KIRKLAND, WA

DR. JORGE BADILLO-COCHRAN
607 MARKET ST., KIRKLAND, WA

DR. JONATHAN COLLIN
12911 120TH AVE. N.E., #A-50, KIRKLAND, WA

DR. LESTER E. GRIFFITH
19514 64TH AVE. W., LYNNWOOD, WA

DR. DOROTHY L. JOHNSON
18119 36TH AVE. W., APT. K102, LYNNWOOD, WA

DR. LYNDON C. CAPON
16504 6TH AVE. W., LYNNWOOD, WA

DR. MICHAEL EBERLE
1603 3RD ST., MARYSVILLE, WA

DR. MICHAEL MILES
515 CEDAR AVE., MARYSVILLE, WA

DR. GARY A. BACHMAN
1910 RIVERSIDE DR., STE. 5, MOUNT VERNON, WA

DR. MARK GIGNAC
5802 224TH PL. S.W., MOUNTLAKE TERRACE, WA

DR. ANDREA BLACK
P.O. BOX 1053, OKANOGAN, WA

DR. MAGDA MISCHE
P.O. BOX 22, OLGA, WA

DR. JON DUNN
2617 12TH CT. S.W., #6, OLYMPIA, WA

DR. JENNY DEMEAUZ
3520C SUNSET BEACH DR. N.W., OLYMPIA, WA

DR. JENNIFER BOOKER
203 4TH AVE. E., STE. 305-306, OLYMPIA, WA

DR. JOHN L. BROTTEM
413 LILLY RD. N.E., OLYMPIA, WA

DR. ROBIN E. MOORE
3627 ENSIGN RD. N.E., STE. 8, OLYMPIA, WA

DR. DOROTHY KARCHESKI
2622 PACIFIC AVE. S.E., STE. C, OLYMPIA, WA

DR. CURTIS ALLEN-GRANT
20803 ORVILLE RD. E., ORTING, WA

DR. JONATHAN COLLIN
911 TYLER ST., PORT TOWNSEND, WA

DR. LINDA SHOWLER
P.O. BOX 466, PORT TOWNSEND, WA

DR. JOSEPH DISPENZA
P.O. BOX 656, RAINIER, WA

DR. ALBERT G. CORRADO
750 SWIFT BLVD., STE. 22, RICHLAND, WA

DR. REBECCA WYNSOME
3931 BRIDGE WAY N., SEATTLE, WA

DR. ERIC S. JONES
1307 N. 45TH ST., STE. 200, SEATTLE, WA

DR. MORGAN MARTIN
2705 E. MADISON ST., SEATTLE, WA

DR. M. J. GUILTINAN
1307 N. 45TH ST., STE. 200, SEATTLE, WA

DR. DONALD BROWN
3644 BAGLEY AVE. N., SEATTLE, WA

DR. DOUG LEWIS
9111 ROOSEVELT WAY N.E., SEATTLE, WA

DR. MARIE R. ADAMS
3931 BRIDGE WAY N., SEATTLE, WA

DR. MARK D. GROVEN
1307 N. 45TH ST., STE. 200, SEATTLE, WA

DR. JEANA D. KIMBALL
1911 11TH AVE. E., SEATTLE, WA

DR. JULIA A. TYSON
200 W. MERCER ST., STE. 508, SEATTLE, WA

DR. CATHY A. ROGERS
900 MADISON ST., SEATTLE, WA

DR. MARY RICHTER
901 BOREN AVE., STE. 1530, SEATTLE, WA

DR. ESTEBAN RYCIAK
1532 PIKE PL., SEATTLE, WA

DR. CHARLES HAMILTON
301 N. 67TH ST., SEATTLE, WA

DR. W. F. WULSIN
753 N. 35TH ST., STE. 302, SEATTLE, WA

DR. WILLIAM A. MITCHELL
518 1ST AVE N., STE. 28, SEATTLE, WA

DR. RALPH A. PASCUALY
550 16TH AVE., STE.304, SEATTLE, WA

DR. DAN LABRIOLA
1020 E. JOHN ST., SEATTLE, WA

DR. STEPHEN J. KING
5502 34TH AVE. N.E., SEATTLE, WA

DR. LARALEE JASPER-LITOV
804 N. 43RD ST., #5, SEATTLE, WA

DR. FRANCINE LOEB
7201 5TH AVE. N.E., SEATTLE, WA

DR. KENNETH HARMON
1835 S.W. 152ND ST., SEATTLE, WA

DR. JOANNA T. FORWELL
4800 PHINNEY AVE. N., APT. 6, SEATTLE, WA

DR. RALPH GOLAN
7522 20TH AVE. N.E., SEATTLE, WA

DR. PETER WRIGHT
345 15TH AVE. E., STE. 202, SEATTLE, WA

DR. DOROTHEA DURWOOD
343 N. 103RD ST., SEATTLE, WA

DR. SHERYL R. KIPNIS
5502 34TH AVE. N.E., SEATTLE, WA

DR. MICHAEL G. VESELAGO
217 N. 125TH ST., SEATTLE, WA

DR. NANCY MERCER
7114 ROOSEVELT WAY N.E., SEATTLE, WA

DR. NANCY ROBERTS
14546 GREENWOOD AVE. N., SEATTLE, WA

DR. JANET BEST
3017 N.W. 60TH ST., SEATTLE, WA

DR. MICHAEL B. VARON
11842 31ST PL. N.E., #B, SEATTLE, WA

DR. ROBERT MAY
4020 48TH AVE. S., SEATTLE, WA

DR. RICHARD A. POSMANTUR, JR.
2705 E. MADISON ST., SEATTLE, WA

DR. CHRISTINE MESHEW
1107 N.E. 45TH ST., STE. 100, SEATTLE, WA

DR. LIN CHUN-MING
815 S. WELLER ST., STE. 107A, SEATTLE, WA

DR. ROBERT SCHORE
7715 MERIDIAN AVE. N., SEATTLE, WA

DR. DAVID R. ANDERSON
310 N.W. 82ND ST., SEATTLE, WA

DR. IRVIN H. MILLER
3554 W. SMITH ST., SEATTLE, WA

DR. JOSEPH E. PIZZORNO, JR.
144 N.E. 54TH ST., SEATTLE, WA

DR. ELLEN GOLDMAN
2024 S. DEARBORN ST., SEATTLE, WA

DR. MAURICE WERNESS
2031 N.W. 60TH ST., SEATTLE, WA

DR. PATRICK M. DONOVAN
207 N.W. 73RD ST., SEATTLE, WA

DR. JOHN W. GEORGE
10212 5TH AVE. N.E., STE 230, SEATTLE, WA

DR. ROBERT W. ULLMAN
4072 9TH AVE. N.E., SEATTLE, WA

DR. JOHN B. BASTYR
735 10TH AVE. E., SEATTLE, WA

DR. MARY L. BOVE
3110 N.E. 125TH ST, SEATTLE, WA

DR. LEANNA STANDISH
801 34TH AVE., SEATTLE, WA

DR. ANN McCOMBS
6327 21ST AVE. N.E., SEATTLE, WA

DR. AMY LIND
4141 CALIFORNIA AVE. S.W., SEATTLE, WA

DR. KRISTA HERON
5502 34TH AVE. N.E., SEATTLE, WA

DR. MARK J. LAMDEN
6204 8TH AVE. N.W., SEATTLE, WA

DR. LESLIE J. VANROMER
415 N. SEQUIM AVE., SEQUIM, WA

DR. KIMBERLY KELLY
6729 180TH ST. S.E., SNOHOMISH, WA

DR. JEFFREY C. ELMER
P.O. BOX 2555, SPOKANE, WA

DR. EARL MOORE
711 W. JOSEPH AVE., SPOKANE, WA

DR. HAROLD DICK
1137 W. GARLAND AVE., SPOKANE, WA

DR. LEO M. SCOTT
122 N. ARGONNE RD., STE. 3, SPOKANE, WA

DR. WILLIAM LOOMIS
111 E. CENTRAL AVE., SPOKANE, WA

DR. ROGER ROWSE
1301 N. PINES RD., SPOKANE, WA

DR. BURTON B. HART
12104 E. MAIN AVE., SPOKANE, WA

DR. MELANIE WHITTAKER
30107 68TH AVE. N.W., STANWOOD, WA

DR. THOMAS J. YOUNG
8909 GRAVELLY LAKE DR. S.W., TACOMA, WA

DR. PATTI ROBBINS
1653 E. 31ST ST., TACOMA, WA

DR. OWEN W. MILLER
2611 N. STEVENS ST., TACOMA, WA

DR. IAN MARSH
10216 PATTERSON ST. S., TACOMA, WA

DR. PAUL E. REILLY
5702 N. 26TH ST., STE. C, TACOMA, WA

DR. RUSSELL KOLBO
919 S. 10TH ST., TACOMA, WA

DR. MEED A. WEST
1612 N.E. 78TH ST., VANCOUVER, WA

DR. FRAN BROOKS
P.O. BOX 1921, VASHON, WA

DR. PATRICIA SCOTT
29761 128TH AVE. S.W., VASHON, WA

DR. BILL GIBBON
P.O. BOX 246, WASHOUGAL, WA

DR. GLENN R. HOEY
310 S. MISSION ST., WENATCHEE, WA

DR. MURRAY L. BLACK
609 S. 48TH AVE., YAKIMA, WA

DR. KAITEN RIVERS
811 W. YAKIMA AVE., STE. 105, YAKIMA, WA

DR. RANDALL E. WILKINSON
302 S. 12TH AVE., YAKIMA, WA

DR. ELMER M. CRANTON
15246 LEONA DR. S.E., YELM, WA

WEST VIRGINIA

DR. PRUDENCIO C. CORRO
251 STANAFORD RD., BECKLEY, WV

DR. STEVE M. ZEKAN
1208 KANAWHA BLVD. E., CHARLESTON, WV

DR. DELENO H. WEBB, III
401 11TH ST., STE. 701, HUNTINGTON, WV

DR. KERRY BERTSCHINGER
2002 TUSCARORA PIKE, MARTINSBURG, WV

DR. MARK MYERS
P.O. BOX 27, MOUNT ZION, WV

DR. ALBERT V. JELLEN
2097 NATIONAL RD., WHEELING, WV

WISCONSIN

DR. RALPH BRZEZINSKI
238 N. MAIN ST., ADAMS, WI

DR. KEVIN C. GARRETT
1818 N. MEADE ST., APPLETON, WI

DR. ROGER HASBROUCK
915 MADISON ST., BEAVER DAM, WI

DR. JOHN STEVENSON
P.O. BOX 13508, GREEN BAY, WI

DR. THOMAS J. LEUTHNER
1792 E. MASON ST., GREEN BAY, WI

DR. ELEAZAR M. KADILE
1538 BELLEVUE ST., GREEN BAY, WI

DR. RICHARD L. VANDER HEYDEN
2313 S. WEBSTER AVE., GREEN BAY, WI

DR. DAVID MORRIS
615 10TH ST. S, LA CROSSE, WI

DR. ALAN D. PRATT
1836 SOUTH AVE., LA CROSSE, WI

DR. GEORGE F. KROKER
P.O. BOX 2408, LA CROSSE, WI

DR. VIJAY K. SABINS
P.O. BOX 2408, LA CROSSE, WI

DR. RATHNA ALWA
717 GENEVA ST., LAKE GENEVA, WI

DR. STEVEN M. WEBER
600 HIGHLAND AVE., MADISON, WI

DR. ROSEMARY RAU-LEVINE
3602 ATWOOD AVE., MADISON, WI

DR. GABRIELLE LADEN
301 S. BEDFORD ST., STE. 5, MADISON, WI

DR. TIMOTEO L. GALVEZ
2705 MARSHALL CT., MADISON, WI

DR. KEVIN RUGGLES
1000 N. OAK AVE., MARSHFIELD, WI

DR. ANTHONY J. SWEENEY
8989 N. PORT WASHINGTON., #221, MILWAUKEE, WI

DR. DEAN E. GOBLIRSCH
9900 W. BLUEMOUND RD., MILWAUKEE, WI

DR. JERRY N. YEE
2505 N. MAYFAIR RD., MILWAUKEE, WI

DR. PAUL A. NAUSIEDA
P.O. BOX 503, MILWAUKEE, WI

DR. MARVIN R. WOOTEN
2025 E. NEWPORT AVE., MILWAUKEE, WI

DR. MICHAEL N. KATZOFF
2900 W. OKLAHOMA AVE., MILWAUKEE, WI

DR. DAVID ARNOLD
2900 W. OKLAHOMA AVE., MILWAUKEE, WI

DR. CHRISTINE KRSKO
4227 W. FOREST HOME AVE., MILWAUKEE, WI

DR. ALAN W. SPAETH
8200 W. APPLETON AVE., MILWAUKEE, WI

DR. JAMES GRIB
P.O. BOX 533, MONROE, WI

DR. MARK BOHL
310 E. MAIN ST., MOUNT HOREB, WI

DR. STEVEN J. CARINI
222 N. FRANKLIN ST, PORT WASHINGTON, WI

DR. IRENE PARENT
1117 ARTHUR AVE., RACINE, WI

DR. MARTA W. ENGEL
RR 1 BOX 1198, SOLDIERS GROVE, WI

DR. ORVAL HIDDE
1434 E. MAIN ST., WATERTOWN, WI

DR. WAYNE KONETZKE
403 N. GRAND AVE., WAUKESHA, WI

WYOMING

DR. GERALD L. SMITH
5320 EDUCATION DR., CHEYENNE, WY

DR. MICHAEL LANG
1657 RIVERSIDE DR., LARAMIE, WY